WOKE UP

Nadia Gilkes

 eLegal Publishing
An Imprint of eLegal Cafe, LLC
1527 W State Highway 114, Ste. 500-189
Grapevine, TX 76051

First printing, 2019

Cover Concept and Design by Aerica Raven Van Dorn

Interior Design by Van-Garde Imagery, Inc.

ISBN   978-1-7332504-8-1 (paperback)
        978-1-7332504-7-4 (ebook)

Preface

How'd this book come about?

While traveling in the early part of 2015, I woke up in my window seat in a fit of laughter from my dream. I quickly jotted down the premise. That dream eventually became the basis for this novella. A few months after I started writing this story my mother became ill. After caring for and losing her, I shelved this project because I felt the subject matter would be too uncomfortable for family and friends still grieving her death.

After shelving it for nearly two years I heard about this amazing challenge called NaNoWriMo (**Na**tional **No**vel **Wri**ting **Mo**nth) from friend and fellow Toastmaster Andi Scully. NaNoWriMo is a nonprofit organization that challenges individuals to write a 50,000 word novel during the month of November. That equates to about 200 pages. My interest was piqued but I wasn't completely sold. Months later I had the pleasure of going to lunch with Macario James, a Facebook friend, who casually mentioned that he was also participating in NaNoWriMo.

Hearing about the challenge a second time got my attention. When things "repeat" in my life I take that as a sign that I need to go in that direction. Right there on the spot my decision was made. On October 27th I committed to the 2017 NaNoWriMo challenge; except, I didn't want to write a 200 page novel. I only wanted to write a short story of about 100 pages, so I committed to 25,000 words. I guess you can say I half-jumped in.

During the first four days of the challenge I worked feverishly on a book I want to pen on caregiving but it proved too emotional and required too much research for the short time span of the challenge. Then an idea hit me and I decided to revisit this dream I'd had years ago. On day five of the NaNoWriMo challenge I set the caregiving book aside, jumped into this novel, and never looked back.

Why Now?

Have you heard the sentiment: the graveyard is the richest property in the world, because so many unrealized dreams are buried there?

Time and time again I have put my dreams aside. I've been my biggest roadblock. During a conversation with Marie O'Connor, another Toastmaster, she looked me in the eye and said "perfection is stopping you." She was right. My quest for perfection often leaves my work unseen and my dreams unrealized.

My mother's death taught me many lessons, the most important one being: Life Is Short. It's cliché, but it's true. In the grand scheme, our time on earth passes by in a blink. I don't want to take unfulfilled dreams with me when my time on earth ends. So, why now? Because when it comes to pursuing dreams the time should always be NOW. The outcome doesn't *have* to be perfect. It just needs to be realized.

A few months before my mom passed she said, "you all have done well in life and I'm proud of you all. But there are a lot of opportunities out there. Reach up and grab 'em." So here's to taking mom's advice and grabbing opportunities. I hope you all enjoy reading this novella as much as I enjoyed dreaming and crafting it for you. Above all else, I hope you are inspired to breathe life into your own dreams. You never know who you might inspire, or where the journey might take you.

To those who always stand by my side no matter what crazy dream pops into my head, I thank you for your unwavering support.

This book is lovingly dedicated to

Virginia Wheeler Anglin

1940 - 2016

You are the best mom I ever had ...

I'm walking uphill, both ways it hurts
I bury my heart here in this dirt
I hope it's a seed, I hope it works

I need to grow, here I could be
Closer to light, closer to me
I don't have to do this perfectly

Have I the courage to change

Artist: P!nk
Album: Hurts 2B Human
Track 8: Courage
Composers: Alecia Moore,
Sia Furler,
Greg Kurstin
2019

Part One

Chapter 1

Present Day

The day I woke up dead was the day my life changed forever. Yeah - you read that right. Lol. I mean, I can laugh about it now. It was no laughing matter then. A few years ago I actually woke up at my own funeral. How is that even possible, you ask? Trust me, I've asked that same question myself. I've never received the full story. Some details I've been able to piece together. Some details I gave up ever learning. Here's what I've gathered.

I was sick. I'd been under the weather for a couple weeks but pressed on like I always did. I'm single. Chronically single. With no one to share the load, downtime is a luxury I simply cannot afford. On most days I go about my daily grind giving myself the usual pep talk: "I HAVE to work. I have bills to pay. Rest is overrated. I'll sleep when I'm dead."

At least, that USED to be my mantra. Not so much anymore. Anyhow, I had symptoms of the common cold. It could have even been bronchitis, but I never felt bad enough to go to a doctor. I know my body and this didn't feel serious. I doubled up on my holistic meds and vitamins and kept going. Until one day, I couldn't. I remember waking up and my body just ached. I tried to make it to the kitchen to get some water, and I guess my body just gave out. I collapsed right there on the kitchen floor.

I don't know for sure how long I was out but the consensus seems to be about two days. I don't talk to anyone regularly so that determination was based on my Facebook postings. I post religiously, daily. There was a 53 hour lapse between my last post and the time the landlord unlocked my door for the police wellness check. Somewhere in there I slipped into a coma. By the time paramedics arrived my heart rate and breathing were nearly nonexistent, so naturally they thought I was dead. The medical examiner was called in to do his rituals, then I was shipped off ... to the morgue! I still can't figure out how several departments and numerous people missed the fact that I was sick, but not DEAD! Apparently there's a lot more incompetence in this world than I realized.

Whatever took place at the morgue has never been revealed to me. Every inquiry I made was met with the brick wall of HIPAA laws, privacy policies, and office procedures. I can't tell you how many times in the past year I've screamed,

"It's MY privacy you're supposed to protect and I'M giving you permission to tell ME what happened to ME when I was laid up in your morgue!" Needless to say, I'm still fighting that fight. I guess somewhere along the way, they froze me. Or maybe just kept me slightly chilled. Aside from what's shown on tv dramas, I really have no idea what goes on in those mysterious places. I just thank God no one asked for an autopsy. That probably would have done me in for real.

Once I arrived at the funeral home I was put in the care of an inept embalmer. Somewhere between his penchant for cocaine and loose lady visitors, he failed to embalm me for the service which was quickly scheduled to take place mere days after I arrived. Thank God for another big miracle! Who knew sex on the job could be a life saver? Ultimately, his actions would cost him his career ... and his marriage, but the distraction of his side chick saved my life.

After his part of the process was "complete," I rolled down the rest of the assembly line. Hair, makeup, outfit, arrangements, then it was on to my big day. That's what I've been able to piece together from various accounts. Now let me take you back to how it all started, from my perspective.

Friday, July 11, 2014

I am in the most comfortable bed EVER having the best sleep of my life. However, interrupting my sleep is this awful dream. I can't see any images but I can hear clearly. It sounds like I'm at a funeral - but not a good one. It's one of those crappy funerals where the rent-a-pastor is giving a generic eulogy for someone he clearly doesn't know. I hate these services. So disgraceful. To top it off, this minister has an annoying voice I can't seem to shake or wake up from. I sneeze and turn over on my side. Just as I begin to think, *how'd I even wind up on my back? I never sleep on my back.* I hear a series of screams. *Hmm. That's odd.* I think to myself. I sneeze again and immediately hear a big thud and more screams.

Every time I move I hear a scream. I can't make sense of how I hear everything so vividly, but it's pitch black. My room doesn't normally get THIS dark. Even in the middle of the night a streetlight shines through the window. Something's not right.

As the grogginess fades, I stretch and yawn. Simultaneously, I hear that annoying pastor voice yell, "WHAT THE FUCK!" as the frenzied patter of feet running in various directions surround me. Initially it sounded like I was at a funeral, but now it sounds like I'm in the middle of an earthquake. Things are crashing to the floor, glass is breaking, and there appears to be a stampede happening. My bed starts to rock from side to side. I start to panic. If there is an earthquake, I need to get out of here! I let out a phlegm-filled cough which is met with blood curdling screams. This shocks me fully awake. I immediately try to make sense of why there are so many people in my apartment screaming. Then it dawns on me, *We're in an emergency! They must be trying to rescue me!*

I roll onto my back and try to sit up but immediately hit my head on something above me. It's soft like a pillow, but I can't move it. Now I'M the one thinking "What the fuck??!?" Still trying to make sense of my situation, I reason that items must have crashed on top of me. Thankfully, I'm in an air pocket where I can breathe and move around a little. I reach my hands up and try to push on whatever is above me. When I do a sliver of light shines to my right. I push up again, this time closer to the light and open what appears to be a lid. For a brief moment I consider that maybe I've overreacted. Maybe I just fell asleep in a tanning bed. Then I remember that I don't tan, I'm Black.

With the lid fully open I can finally sit up and get a good stretch. As I do this I hear more screams and items crashing to the floor. I look around and experience my worst nightmare. Nope, I'm not in my bedroom. I'm not in a tanning bed. I'm in a casket! Set up in a chapel! The few people still conscious are staring at me with bewildered looks as if I've done something wrong. I guess I have. I woke up at my own funeral. *Fuck! How did THIS happen?*

As my vision clears I see the aftermath of my awakening. Except for the pews bolted to the floor, the rest of the chapel looks like the epicenter of an earthquake. Floral arrangements and decorations are knocked over. Pictures once neatly hung are now piles of broken glass on the floor. People, either unconscious or injured, litter the aisles. My initial reaction is shock. Shock quickly turns to horror as my eyes settle on my mom in the front row clutching her chest and gasping for air.

Finally, I look down at myself. I'm wearing a fitted, emerald green, floor length dress better suited for someone playing bridesmaid at an evening wedding than star of a funeral. *Who picked this? When in the world do I ever wear green? Uhhhh, never.*

Straight ahead of me rests a big bouquet of yellow roses. *Who the hell picked yellow?!? I hate yellow even more than I hate green!* I scoff and shake my head. What's missing is most egregious of all. I'm supposed to have a Buffalo Bills themed funeral, yet there's not a balloon, banner, or flag bearing their iconic logo.

There is a modest amount of floral arrangements. At this point they're all knocked over, but I am touched by the warm regards. It's sweet to know a few people actually do care. Then I look at the outside of my casket and erupt like a volcano. "A wood grained casket!! Are you kidding me!?! You couldn't pick anything better than this!!!! I HAVE MONEY!!"

Just as I begin my tirade I see a woman gliding slowly towards me with a Bible tucked under her arm and a bottle of Anointing Oil in her hands. She's speaking in tongues. As she approaches she starts to spread oil on her fingers. I don't know who she is, but I do know exactly what she plans to do. When she gets within arm's length, I slap her. Not a hard slap. I don't have a lot of energy. Just enough to stop her in her tracks and quiet her. For a moment she just stands there looking dazed. Her arms drop to her sides. The Bible and uncapped oil fall to the floor, then she turns and floats away as ceremoniously as she came.

At this point, a person I presume is the funeral home director gets up from the floor, where he is fanning one of his funeral attendants, and rushes to my side. He tries in vain to get me to lie down and reassures me everything is going to be all right. "I'm in a fucking casket and I'm alive! Nothing about this is all right!!?" I'm still in volcano mode. The more he tries to soothe and quiet me, the louder I get. "Your whole business is putting on a funeral for dead people! You put on a whole funeral for me and never realized I'M NOT DEAD! I have no confidence in your abilities. Take your hands off me. YOU JUST WAIT TIL I YELP THIS!!!"

Realizing he is not going to be able to calm me, he leaves my side and returns to his attendant still passed out on the floor. I try to climb out of the casket, but it's unsteady and feels like it might tip over. Without help I can't get out. All I can do is sit there and yell.

Chapter 2

In the midst of all the chaos someone actually had enough sense to call for an ambulance. Paramedics arrive to tend to the fallen and cart my mom and me to the hospital - for different reasons, obviously. She looks like she is about to die of a heart attack, I am unexpectedly alive. Once they load me into the ambulance and put the vehicle in drive I scream, "Are the lights and sirens on? I think after all this I deserve lights and sirens." They assure me that I'm getting my money's worth and vow to get me to the hospital as quickly as possible. "How does this happen?" I keep repeating. "How did so many people not realize I was still alive? And if I woke up a few hours later I would have been BURIED ALIVE!!" The paramedics take a considerable amount of time trying to hook up an IV. They eventually find a suitable vein in my foot and push some fluids into me. I suspect a sedative is added as well. They do their best to calm me down and take my vitals as we race to the hospital.

In the emergency room I am seen immediately. The ER

doctor hears wheezing in my chest and orders x-rays. The diagnosis is walking pneumonia which I find ironic since I haven't walked anywhere in a week. Aside from that and dehydration I am deemed in great shape for being dead. Turns out I have fat to spare. I could probably be "dead" for another week and still survive.

The ER doctor lists me in stable condition, at least physically, and admits me for observation and treatment. "A few rounds of antibiotics and you'll be good as new in no time," he declares.

"Well that's good to know. A few hours ago I was dead and in my casket so things are certainly looking up," I quip.

"Hmmm …," he says and leaves the room. Clearly he doesn't want any part of that conversation.

After a couple hours in the ER, a hospital bed becomes available and I am wheeled up to my room. I make sure everyone I pass knows of my good fortune. "I'm going backwards. I had my funeral a few hours ago and now I'm getting admitted to the hospital!" They very likely thought I was a lunatic heading to the psych ward soon after my ailment was cured. Little did they know.

Once in my room they transfer me to the permanent bed and hook up my wires to the room's monitoring machines. Not long after I get situated some family members begin to show up. They are eerily quiet. Not at all characteristic of our family. No one, including me, knows what to say.

After 15 minutes of awkward silence together, a doctor

softly knocks on my door, walks over to my bedside, and introduces himself as Dr. Shakir. Three residents follow closely like ducklings and he asks if I will permit them to observe my exam. I nod and they huddle excitedly around my chart. Turns out my situation makes a great, live case study and Dr. Shakir wants to use this as a teaching moment. I am poked and prodded and discussed as if I'm a cadaver. Normal doctor bedside manner, but in this instance - ironic. I came very close to actually BEING a cadaver! I can't completely wrap my mind around my reality yet. I just know my situation sucks.

I sit up in my hospital bed listening intently to the doctors give their theories on how this could have happened. Eventually I get fed up and put my head in my hands. When I feel my head I notice something doesn't feel right. "Is my hair straightened?" I mutter. "Oo I know my hair's not straightened!" I stop the doctor mid-sentence and ask for a mirror. To my horror, my hair is flat-ironed. "Who straightened my hair?" No reply. "Who in the hell straightened my hair!!?! If I wash my hair and my curls don't come back there will be Hell. To. Pay!" My youngest brother Brandon assures me I am 'focusing on the wrong thing.' Meanwhile a nurse rushes in to put a sedative in my IV. I try to resist but she moves at lightning speed.

Again, I am out for an unknown length of time. When I come to, my family is gone but a mystery woman sits at my bedside. She is thin and pale with jet black hair in a precision bob. She is well dressed but her clothes fit a little too big. Her makeup is carefully applied but fails to soften her harsh features. To sum it up, she looks gaunt, ghostly, and terrified.

When she realizes I'm awake she stands, a bit unsteadily in her heels, and gingerly approaches me. She places her hands on top of mine and asks what my initial feelings are. I snap, "I woke up at my funeral, so initially I'm feeling like I need to sue somebody. How do you think I feel?" Hearing this, she seems to get even more pale than she already was. Finally, she gets around to introducing herself.

"My name is AnnaBelle Koreg. Most people call me AK. I'm one of the staff psychiatrists here at Springfield Memorial Hospital. Dr. Shakir requested that I come chat with you about your circumstance."

Blank stare from me.

"Your situation is quite unique. I'm sure you have a lot of uncertain feelings swirling around," she says hesitantly.

Still staring blankly.

"It's completely understandable if you don't want to talk right now. I'm sure you'd like to get some rest —"

I cut her off. "Apparently I've already been resting for about a week. I don't need rest, and I don't need a psychiatrist. What I need is to get up and let people know I'm alive and figure out my next steps."

"Yeah. Ok. Well why don't I just leave my card. When you're feeling up to it, you can give me a call and we can set up an appointment." She places her card on my nightstand and scuttles out of the room. Soon after she leaves I hear quiet chatter in the hallway. These fools don't even have enough sense to walk away from my door before they start talking about me. I roll my eyes and reach for the remote.

I turn on the tv and start to flip channels. Nothing interests me, not even the SVU marathon. I can't stop my mind from racing. This whole thing is just so fucked up. I reach for my phone and realize I don't have one. I guess it's still home. I'll have someone get that for me in the morning. *Ugh. I hate being without it.* I ring the call button. The nurse comes promptly and I ask if there is a business lounge anywhere in the hospital. To my surprise, there is. I start to get out of bed and she quickly runs to my side. "Whoa! WHOA! Easy there. You can't get out of bed without assistance." I tell her I'm fine ... and then nearly fall to the floor. She gives me a hand back into bed. "You haven't been on your feet in a week. You've got to take it slow. Sit tight and I'll have someone come and wheel you to the business center."

I sit on the edge of the bed and massage my legs. *I have too much to do. I can't take it slow. I have to get back to my life.* About 10 minutes later Nurse Nick comes with a wheelchair. He helps me out of bed and transfers my IV bag to the wheelchair pole. We make our way down to the second floor where the business center is.

I choose a computer and try Facebook. My first few login attempts are unsuccessful. Auto login is a gift and a curse at the same time. It's nice to stay logged in on your personal devices. However, on the rare occasion you are away from your device it's a struggle to remember your passwords. When I finally get access to my account, it's frozen! I'd set up a legacy account contact. In the event of my death, my designated person would be notified that they have access to my account and can post on my behalf. The contact is not given my login information, but I guess Facebook figures once a user is dead they won't be logging in again and now I'm getting a warning message. After a series of questions to verify that I am the actual account holder, I'm given access. When my page finally loads, it's barren. All my pictures and posts are gone. All that's displayed is a flickering candle as the profile picture and lots of RIP messages. *FUCK! I had some good pictures on there.* I'm going to have to figure out how to retrieve my page contents. Hopefully it's not permanently deleted. I grab a pen and a slip of paper and start jotting down a To Do List:

To Do List

- Contact Facebook to retrieve my page contents.

Now it's time to fix this gross miscommunication. Everyone thinks I died. A quick Facebook post will quickly let everyone know I'm all right. I post:

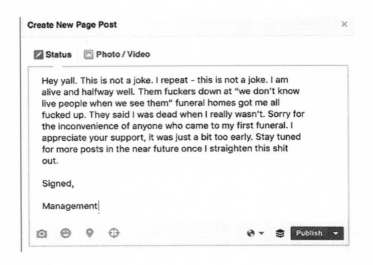

I click the globe to make my status public. Then, 'Post.' *There! That should do it.* I log out.

Next, I try to check my email. No matter how hard I try I can't remember the password for anything. I sit there staring at the gmail screen for an eternity. After a while another idea comes to mind. Since I'm "dead," I might as well look up my obituary. I visit the website for *The Springfield News*, our local newspaper, to check out obits for the past week. I find mine and immediately burst into tears. Not only is it absolutely weird to see my own obituary, but I hate my picture. Of all the pictures I had posted on Facebook THIS is the one my family chose.

I pull out my running to-do list to add to it:

<u>To Do List</u>

- Contact Facebook to retrieve my page contents.
- Find out who chose the obit profile picture and cuss them out!

I compose myself and turn my attention back to the obituary. It's short. Just your basic blurb:

> Hope Allison (HAM) McKinley, 34, of
> Springfield, KS passed away on July 7, 2014
> of natural causes. She is survived by her
> loving parents Edward & Evelyn McKinley, Sr.,
> Brothers Edward, Jr. and Brandon (Seneca)
> McKinley, nieces, aunts, cousins, and her
> beloved piranha Chyna. Viewing will be
> held on Friday, July 11, 2014 from 11:00am-
> NOON at Johnson Family Funeral Homes, 123
> Main Street, Springfield, Kansas. Service to
> immediately follow.

"I call bullshit! Natural causes?? How about NO causes 'cause I'm not dead you ... UGH!!!!" I don't realize I am actually screaming and shaking my fists at the computer until Nurse Nick rushes over to see what is wrong.

He looks on the screen and realizes what I'm doing. "Hey. Maybe now is not the time to look at that. There's no need to get yourself all worked up ..."

"No. No. I'll be fine. I have to know what's out there. I'm sorry I scared you. I'm fine."

Nick takes a little convincing, but he finally goes back to sit in one of the lounge chairs against the wall. I take a few deep breaths and try to find a silver lining. At least they acknowledged Chyna. *Oh my God! Who's feeding Chyna?* I snatch up my to do list and again add to it:

To Do List

- Contact Facebook to retrieve my page contents.
- Find out who chose the obit profile picture and cuss them out!
- Who (if anyone) is taking care of Chyna?

Then, another thought:

- Contact The Springfield News to have them retract the death notice. Make the dumbass funeral home pay for that.

I glance at the obit on the screen once again. I don't know why, but I print the page. Next, I go to the funeral home's website. I find my obituary and guestbook. Same shitty picture but at least the obituary has a little more substance. My career and some of my accomplishments are listed but there's still nothing about my beloved Buffalo Bills. I print this page as well. I peruse the guest book. Forty seven entries in a week. Not bad. A lot of RIPs, she was lovely, sorry for your loss, and comforting Bible verses. I take note of who left messages (and who didn't) and go back to the main page. I click "About Us" and glance at the profiles. I find the owners' names and pull out my running to do list:

- Go by Johnson Family Funeral Homes and pay a visit to Thelma and Frederick Johnson, Jr. IMMEDIATELY!

They owe me some answers. I sit there staring at their picture until every detail is etched in my memory. Not being able to think of anything else to do at the moment, I log off and ask Nurse Nick to take me outside to get some fresh air.

After an hour or so I request to go back to my room. I really don't *want* to go back, but there is nowhere else for me to go. Nurse Nick pushes me through the main lobby and down a long hallway. We come to a bank of elevators and wait for one to arrive. Turns out I'm on the 4th floor.

Once back in my room, Nurse Nick helps me into bed and reattaches the IV and antibiotics to the bed pole. He makes sure I'm comfortable, even getting more blankets when I tell him I'm cold. I've actually been piercingly cold ever since I woke from the coma. As soon as I swaddle myself in blankets, my dinner tray arrives. Dr. Shakir placed me on a restricted diet so there are no choices. Soup, bread, and clear liquids are all I'm allowed. The soup of the evening is creamy chicken and wild rice which actually tastes pretty good. The bread is a plain white roll. Sprite and water round out the meal. When the first spoonful hits my lips I realize I'm actually starving and practically inhale dinner. After the staff removes my dinner tray I request a couple cups of tea to help warm me up.

When everyone is out of the room I place the IV bag on the mobile pole and make my way to the bathroom on my own. I'm still a bit weak but dinner is definitely giving me a boost. I make the 15-foot trek to and from the bathroom without incident and settle back in bed for the night. *I've gotta get out of here*, I think to myself. *Tomorrow I'm going home!* I snuggle under the covers and start to flip through channels. The night nurse returns with my tea and asks if I want something to help me sleep. I tell her no, the tea will be sufficient. "OK, dear, well just push the button if you need anything else." She's sweet. I didn't catch her name but she's one of the most genuine nurses I've encountered since I've been here.

I scan all the tv channels and finally settle on the continuous stream of mindless game shows. I lower the volume, sip on the tea a while longer, and try to snooze. Every time I start to doze off, I jerk awake. Even though I'm exhausted my body refuses to let me sleep. I consider taking the nurse up on her offer of a sedative and immediately break into a cold sweat. *What in the world is happening to me?* My mind races as I wonder what will happen next. I don't even know the depths of issues I'll have to unravel. I wish more than anything that this is all just a bad dream.

While I'm lying here with nothing to do and unable to focus, I wish I had some product to wash my hair. I want to make sure my curls come back. I pull out my to-do list to add to it yet again:

To Do List

- Contact Facebook to retrieve my page contents.

- Find out who chose the obit profile picture and cuss them out!

- Who (if anyone) is taking care of Chyna?

- Contact The Springfield News to have them retract the death notice. Make the dumbass funeral home pay for that.

- Go by Johnson Family Funeral Homes and pay a visit to Thelma and Frederick Johnson, Jr. IMMEDIATELY!

- Make a hair appointment for a wash, condition, and low maintenance up-do

Chapter 3

Saturday, July 12, 2014

The nurse comes in around 3:00AM to add medicine to my IV line. I feign sleep because the thought of a sedative scares me half to death. A quick check of the machines and she turns on her heels and bounces out of the room. I go back to staring at the tv. The hours tick by. When I see the sky changing from pitch black to a beautiful burnt orange, tears come to my eyes. *What if I hadn't awakened in time?* Another chill runs through my body.

Around 7:00AM a nurse skips in with a robe, shower shoes, and towels. She offers to help me take a shower. I ease out of bed and tell her that I'll be fine on my own. "Are you sure?" She looks doubtful. "Positive," I state. She points out the emergency signal and encourages me to use it if I need assistance. She places a toiletry kit on the sink and I go about my daily grooming. In the shower I'm careful not to get too much of my hair wet, but I do run some water over a small portion at the nape of my neck. When I finally step out of the shower I look in the mirror and see a slight wave, but not really a "curl." *Hmmph. Be patient,* I tell myself. Sometimes it takes a bit of time for the curl pattern to return after the hair has been straightened. God only knows how much they fried my hair since they were dealing with a dead person and all. It *is* styled in a very elegant updo though. Whoever did my hair did a great job. Maybe I should make the funeral home hairstylist my new go-to.

I dry off, lotion, put on the fresh robe and slowly make my way out of the bathroom. An aide is changing the sheets so I sit in one of the visitor chairs until she is done. When she leaves I crawl back into bed. By the time I get settled, break-fast arrives. Still on a restricted diet, I am given oatmeal, a side of eggs, and a piece of white bread. Not toast - dry, cold bread. A side of apple juice and water are the beverages. I opt for the oatmeal and juice and push the rest aside. When I'm done with breakfast I drift off to sleep. I hear muffled voices every now and then but am too exhausted to fully awaken. When I finally come back around it's 2:36PM. I feel refreshed and more clear-headed than I've been since first being admitted to the hospital.

At 3:45PM Dr. Shakir pops in with his resident duck-lings in tow. They review my chart, check my vitals, and ask how I'm feeling. "Great," I say enthusiastically. "I'm all set and ready to go home."

"Well we should be able to arrange that in a couple of days." He says.

"No," I counter. "I'm going home today."

He swiftly looks up from my chart, concerned. "OO no, you need to recuperate a few more days …"

"Look," I cut him off. "We both know there is not enough wrong with me to warrant another night's stay in this hospital. Everyone here treats me with either fear or fascination and I'm sick of both. I will not continue to be your show horse," pointing to the residents standing sheepishly behind him. "I'm leaving today. You can process the discharge papers, or not. Either way I'm walking out of here."

Dr. Shakir makes a lame attempt to disagree, "You still need antibiotics."

I stand firm. "Write a prescription and get my discharge papers ready. You can't hold me against my will, and this is not up for debate."

He sighs and resigns himself to the fact that he really has no authority to get his way. He leaves the room with his ducklings in tow and heads to the nurses' station which is just barely out of earshot.

Forty five minutes later a nurse comes in and goes over a mountain of discharge paperwork with me. The stack is larger than normal since I'm leaving against doctor's orders. She gives me a prescription for my antibiotics and tells me to follow up in a week with my primary care physician.

The only outfit I have is the one I arrived in - the emerald green, floor length gown. A bad choice for a funeral, an even worse choice for discharge attire; but it's this or a hospital gown so I change into the dress, thankful that undergarments are included. The nurse gives me a hospital bag to hold the toiletry kit, my to-do list, and all my paperwork. She asks if I have a ride. I don't actually. No one has visited since those first moments after I was admitted. She arranges for wheelchair transport to the main entrance and calls a taxi for me.

I give the driver my address which is about 20 minutes away from the hospital. When I get to my apartment I ask the taxi driver to wait for a few moments. I don't have my keys, but I keep an extra set taped to the top of the door sill. I know, I know, not the smartest idea. But I've been locked out of my apartment twice so having spare home and car keys easily accessible sure comes in handy. I reach up and grab the keys. I plan to hurry in, get some cash out of the Arm & Hammer box I keep in the freezer, then run back out to pay the driver. I'm sure the tab is still running. It was reaching the $40 mark when I got out of the car. God only knows how much it goes up each minute. I let myself into my apartment and stop cold. My place is completely empty.

Where. The. Fuck. Is. My. STUFF!!! I walk through the entire apartment. There's lint and random trash on the carpet, traces of makeup in the bathroom sink, slight wear and tear on the walls, but no STUFF! I doubt someone found my spare keys, cleaned me out, then put the keys back. That can't be the answer. So where is my stuff! A long, impatient car horn knocks me out of my trance. *FUCK! The taxi driver is still waiting.* I stand in the hallway, hands on my hips, pondering. *What am I going to do?* Another round of car honking jerks me into action. I go out to my car to see how much cash I have in the center console. A whopping $18. I take it to the taxi driver and try to explain my dilemma.

"This is all the money I have access to right now. No, I was not intentionally trying to *rob* you," I reply indignantly. "My apartment has been cleaned out. There is nothing left." I offer to let him come inside so he can see for himself. He waves me off. I can't understand everything he's saying through his thick accent but his yelling and gestures make his anger easy to decipher. When he's done ranting I finally get him to reason. I explain that there's nothing I can do right now. I have to figure out where my stuff is and then I'll be able to pay him later. He snatches the $18 from my grasp and takes down my number. He's not happy, but this is really his only option. If he calls the police they will just confirm that my apartment is empty and there is nothing more I can do for him. He drives off making a lot of gestures as he speeds away. I head to the leasing office.

Chapter 4

I'm a model tenant. I always pay my rent early, rarely ever complain, and go to all the resident appreciation functions. Needless to say, I have a great rapport with the leasing office so I can't understand why they back away from me when I walk through the French doors. Sure I look angry. I should be, I've been robbed! I'm not here to blame *them* for the situation but I definitely plan to demand answers. It doesn't dawn on me that I'm walking around with a messy updo, a bright green evening gown, and a hospital bracelet on. I've also forgotten that everyone thinks I'm dead, apparently including the leasing staff. As the reality of the situation sinks in I dial back my aggression and take a deep breath. The three ladies stare at me. I stare back. I try to determine who is the least freaked out and settle on Stephanie. She's the assistant manager, always friendly, always willing to help, and the one I've interacted with the most. I call her name and move toward her desk. She recoils a little. I stop in my tracks and state the obvious, "We need to talk." I give her a moment to collect herself and she finally nods her head.

I take a seat at Stephanie's desk. The other two ladies watch from their desks, both within earshot. They have no intention of giving us any privacy, and I know I'm going to be office gossip as soon as I leave.

To break the tension I let out a nervous giggle and announce, "Great news! I'm not really dead." All the color instantly drains from her face. I grit my teeth and sigh. Obviously I'm really bad at breaking the tension. After the awkward moment passes I quickly move the conversation along.

"First, I guess I should start by asking what happened from your standpoint." She opens up the file drawer under her desk and pulls out my file. "Well," she says uneasily, "a little over a week ago a relative of yours came by with a police officer to do a wellness check on you. No one could reach you so we escorted the police officer and your brother, I believe?" She pulls out the Emergency Contact Form I filled out when I moved in. "You have Brandon McKinley listed as one of the people able to access your apartment in the event of an emergency?"

"Yes, that's my brother," I reply.

"Yeah, so he came by with an officer, filled out this affidavit, and Rachel let them into your apartment. When she glances to her left, Rachel suddenly starts typing at rapid speed, completely unaware that her computer is in sleep mode. *What a coward of a manager,* I think as I roll my eyes.

Stephanie turns her attention back to me and continues filling in the details. When the door was opened they found you de—," she starts then hesitantly corrects herself, "unresponsive in the kitchen. Paramedics were called but we were told …" She stops. I give her a tense gaze. She looks down at the papers on her desk, unable to face me as she finishes. "We were told that it was too late and the coroner was called to take you away." Now she darts her eyes towards Carla, the other leasing assistant, who now starts shuffling through papers. Stephanie and Carla are closest in age and probably office besties. Regardless, in this moment Carla has nothing to offer her, not even an encouraging glance.

"Well that gives me the back story of how all this got set in motion. Thank you. Now, do you know what happened to all my stuff. My apartment is completely empty."

Stephanie throws another glance at Rachel who is now intently rearranging the contents on her desk. Getting no help, Stephanie returns her attention to me. "A few days after … the wellness check … your brother came back to clear out your apartment. We told him there was no rush, the rent was paid through the end of the month, but he insisted they wanted to go ahead and clear it. We gave him the key because he was listed …," her voice cracks as she points to the Emergency Contact Form. She looks on the verge of tears.

"Stephanie it's all right," I assure her. "You didn't do anything wrong. I'm just trying to figure out what happened so I can track down my things. Now, what's going to happen with my lease? Is it still valid?"

She looks at Rachel and my eyes follow. This time I don't

give her the benefit of quickly looking away to ease her dis-
comfort. I stare at her and wait for her to answer the question
we all know she heard. Finally, she finds her voice, "We'll
fix it. Don't you worry about that. We'll contact our parent
company right away and get the paperwork all straightened
out." She tries to sound upbeat but looks distressed and confused. "Great! That's one less thing I have to worry about."
I let out a sigh of relief, not even realizing I'd been holding
my breath. I start to get up and Stephanie stops me. "Wait!
How are you ... here? I mean. Rachel *saw* you. The coroner
..." I hold up my hand. "That is the million dollar question.
As soon as I can get my things back, I'll be on a mission to
get those answers."

This time I do rise. I thank Stephanie for her help and
make my way towards the exit. Before the door closes all the
way I hear instant chatter. I roll my eyes and head down the
walkway. Back in my empty apartment I feel defeated. I lock
the door behind me, collapse on the living room floor and
cry myself to sleep.

Sunday, July 13, 2014

The next morning I jerk awake when sunlight peeks through
the blinds. Pain greets me as I try to get up. With no bed,
blankets, or pillows I slept in an awkward position. I slowly
make my way off the floor. A good stretch gets the blood cir-
culating so I can walk around my empty apartment. On the

kitchen counter I see my hospital bag. I open it and find my trusty "to-do" list sitting right on top. I pull it out and set it on the bar top. A small stack of paper is folded in half. I open it to reveal my obituary and bios of the funeral director and his wife. A chill runs through my body. I put those on the bar top along with my to-do list. I look through the discharge papers and find my prescription. I have to remember to fill that later today.

All that remains is the toiletry kit. It has everything I need to groom, but I have no towels or change of clothes. I brush my teeth, splash water over my face, put my hair back into place as best I can without a comb or product. I gently position the shower cap over my hair and ease into the shower. I try to use the bar of soap to scrub my body but without a washcloth it's hard to hold. I give up and just let the hot water run over me for a long while. It feels like heaven. I wish I could stay here forever and pretend that I don't have a care in the world but nothing could be further from the truth. I turn off the water and step out the shower where I immediately slip to the floor. My head hits the base of the tub on the way down nearly causing my real death. *UGH!* I pull myself up and get back in the shower to rinse myself off, gingerly stepping out of the shower the second time around. As I air dry I look over myself in the mirror. I pat my head and make sure there's no blood. I don't want to wind up BACK in the hospital explaining this incident.

The teeny bottle of lotion in the kit covers about half my body.

I do what I can and stare at my clothes. Green dress, bra, Spanx, and hospital slippers. I cringe at the thought of having to wear the same clothes again. I try to reason, *Hey, men do it all the time!* That doesn't make me feel any better. I need some clothes. With no other options I get dressed and head to Brandon's house where I'm certain everyone is gathered. It's time to have a family meeting.

On the drive over I make a mental list of issues to discuss. *Where are all my belongings - especially my clothes, phone, and wallet? Why did they empty my apartment out so fast? Why didn't anyone visit me in the hospital? Who's been handling my affairs? Has anyone contacted a probate attorney? Where is Chyna?*

Chapter 5

When I turn onto Brandon's street I see the driveway full of cars, just as I anticipated. I park on the street not too far away. I grip the steering wheel and bow my head to say a small prayer for peace and restraint. When I get to the doorway I find the door already unlocked, likely to accommodate the revolving door of visitors. People who couldn't manage to make their way to the hospital to visit me but could gather here to provide comfort to those "really suffering." The lively chatter ceases as soon as I enter the door. There are audible gasps and someone screams, "O my God!" I'm sure I'm quite a sight standing there in my funeral outfit. A messy hairdo and hospital slippers add drama, no doubt.

"Oh, don't let me stop you. Please, carry on," I say. I hadn't planned to start off with sarcasm but I just couldn't resist. Sarcasm is one of my many gifts. Both of my brothers, nieces, aunts, one cousin, and two people I don't recognize are all gathered in the living room. Some lower their heads and focus on their cellphones. Others look around not knowing what to do or say.

"Well ok, if no one has anything to say, I'll start. We need to have a family meeting." I turn to the two strangers who appear to be a couple. "Who are you?" I ask calmly. The woman is wringing her hands. The man is looking at his phone. When they realize I'm talking to them, they perk up, look at each other, and reply stumbling over each other's words. "Oh, we're friends from church. We came to pray and provide comfort to the family," he finishes.

My sarcasm rears its head again. "That is lovely! So mighty kind of you. Now, prayer works any time, any where, right?"

"Oh, yes," the Mrs. replies jubilantly. "The Lord is all around. He always hears and answers prayers."

"That's wonderful! Well in that case, I'm going to need you to take your prayers elsewhere for the time being. We're about to have a family meeting in here."

"Well, in light of the circumstances, I think it may be beneficial for us to stay and pray with you all before the meeting begins. We may even be able to provide some guidance as you work through everything," the woman reasons.

"Plus, we're blocked in anyway," the husband adds.

I walk slowly toward the couple. Thinly veiled anger in my voice. "I don't care if you have to sit in your car all day. THIS meeting is for family and that does not include you. Now get up, and get out. You can pray about it in your car if that makes you feel better, but you are not welcome here!!"

The husband quickly jumps up and stands between me and his wife. She gathers her purse and phone and they both make a beeline for the door slamming it behind them as they exit. I sit in the spot on the couch they just vacated.

"Now that the riff-raff is gone, let's chat." I take a look around. "Where's Mom?" I ask. Extended silence from everyone in the room. "Anyone who has the same mom as I do, feel free to answer," I say, as I look at both my brothers. Eddie, the oldest of the bunch, pipes up, "She hasn't been feeling well. She's on bed rest while the doctors try to get her blood pressure stabilized. This whole situation has been hard for her." A snort escapes me as I nod my head in understanding. My mom being on bed rest is not funny but, my God, can anyone truly be having a harder time than me?!?

"Ok. I guess it's best we continue to let her rest. So who's in charge? Who's been handling things?" I ask.

Brandon clears his throat. "I guess that'd be me."

"Why did you clear out my apartment so fast?" I insist. "You had 'til the end of the month?"

"We didn't see the point in waiting. Since we were given time off from work we figured it was best to handle everything now."

"So where are my things?" I push.

"Well it's been divided up among —" He starts to explain when suddenly I decide it doesn't really matter.

"You know what? Don't even bother to answer that. I want my stuff ... back in my apartment ... TONIGHT! I don't care what it takes. I will not spend another night sleeping on the floor so make it happen!"

Silence washes over the room again. "Where's my phone?" I ask.

My niece Brynlee chimes in. "Here's your phone right here." She pulls it up from the side of the couch where it's been charging. "There's been lots of messages but we couldn't unlock it. I did answer one call but it was a guy with a thick accent who kept yelling. He's called several times."

At first I'm confused, then I slap my hand to my forehead. *FUCK! I still need to pay the taxi driver.* "Where's my purse?"

"It's upstairs." Brynlee answers as she gets up to retrieve it. She heads up the stairs and turns around a few steps from the top. "Aunt HAM, do you want something else to wear. I have some of your clothes up here." I look down at my funeral clothes. "Yes, that'd be great, sweetie, thank you." She disappears upstairs for about five minutes. When she returns she's dragging a purse and one of my small duffle bags. I smile at the sight of my stuff. Even this little bit brings me joy. I grab a t-shirt, jeans, and flip flops out of the duffle bag. I don't see any underclothes. I run in the half bath to change. I'm stuck with the week-old Spanx but at least I look like a normal person instead of someone late to the ball.

I smooth my hair and head back to the living room. Seeing me in normal clothes seems to put everyone a little more at ease. I stuff my green dress in the duffle bag and throw the hospital slippers in the garbage. A cursory look through my purse shows everything pretty much intact. My wallet and MacBook are there. Spare change. Lots of receipts and random paper. Looks about right.

"Where's Chyna?" I ask as I close my purse back up. My youngest niece Brielle speaks up. "She's in my room. She's so pretty to look at. Are you gonna take her back?" Brielle looks like she's going to cry. I'm sure this week has been rough on her too. I don't want to add to her stress. "No, sweetheart, I'm not going to take her back. You can keep Chyna." A broad smile lights her face.

I place my purse on top of the duffle bag and face every-one. "It would have been nice if someone had stayed by my side while I was in the hospital." Again several people start to speak at once. I patiently wait for them to speak one at a time. Finally Brandon's voice booms through. "We did come by your room a couple times. One time you were sleeping. The other time you weren't in the room. We were trying to make the rounds and visit everybody."

I sit on the edge of the couch and encourage Brandon to continue. "What do you mean *everybody*?" He proceeds to give me an overview of what happened after I woke up unex-pectedly. "Well, Mom had heart palpitations and was admit-ted to the hospital overnight. And you know Aunt Janie has fainting spells. She passed out. Cousin Theo got trampled when people rushed to leave 'cause his fake leg came off and he couldn't get out the way. And Aunt Fannie hit her head on a pew and suffered a mild concussion after someone tipped her wheelchair over. A few other people had mild injuries."

I wish I could say I was filled with compassion and concern. Instead, all I could think was, *I wonder if there's a video on YouTube?* I sit there listening to the rundown completely speechless. It's a miracle I didn't burst out laughing. At least now I had a better explanation for all the noise and earthquake-like aftermath.

"I can understand the need to check on Mom and make sure she was stable, but after that I should have been the priority. Instead I was left to catch a taxi home from the hospital only to find an empty apartment."

Brandon responded, "Well we really didn't expect you to be discharged so soon. The nurse said they expected to keep you for a few days. We were going to come back later this evening to see how you were doing."

"Well, good thing I showed up and saved you the trouble." My sarcasm remains boundless. After an uncomfortable silence I ask, "Is Mom upstairs? I should go see her?"

Brandon jumps up and blocks the path to the stairway. "She's resting. I don't think it's a good idea for you to see her yet. This whole ordeal has really taken a toll on her."

I give him a blank stare as I grab my phone, purse, and duffle bag and make a move towards the door. As I leave I re-state, "I want my things back in my apartment tonight." I slam the door and hear instant chatter as I walk down the stoop. While walking down the driveway I see the church couple sitting in their car trying to pretend they're not eyeing me. I hold my head high, throw the duffel bag in the trunk and hop in the car. Before I can even get my driver door shut they are already out of their car and hightailing it up the stoop. I roll my eyes and speed off. I guess they'll spend the next couple hours praying about the whole situation. They better pray up some furniture in my apartment while they're at it.

Chapter 6

Agitated, I drive around for about an hour ultimately stopping at the mall. I desperately need some new undies and a few other things until my items are returned. I head into Macy's and go straight to the lingerie section. I pick up a week's worth of bras and panties, then head to the sale racks for a few outfits. Since I have time on my hands I pick up a variety of skirts, blouses, and dresses and have fun playing dress up. Five outfits make the cut - three dresses (including a sexy red number), two skirts, and three blouses. A quick browse of the shoe section yields two pairs of heels - one nude, one black. Remembering the slip and fall incident, I grab a set of towels and bathroom rugs on my way to the nearest checkout register.

A petite, unassuming older lady with short, curly, grey hair is working the register. I glance at her name tag and give her a warm greeting. "Hi Edna! How's your day going?"

"It's fine, dear. Did you find everything you need?"

"Yep, I'm all set."

She scans my purchases and it all rings up to just under $400. *Sweet! I love a good deal.* Edna pulls out a sales paper and applies this week's coupon which brings the total down even further to $328.47. I'm ecstatic! I whip out my Macy's card and hand it to the cashier. I hardly ever have time to shop so the balance on my card stays low. For that reason, I'm completely baffled when the card is declined. I know I have $400 available on my card. I should have close to $15,000! "I'm sorry, there must be a mistake. I should have plenty of room on the card. Can you run it again?"

She gives me a curt smile as she runs the card through again. Another alarm rings out notifying anyone nearby that the card is declined. "I don't know how that's possible," I say in disbelief. She lets me know that I can call the number on the back of the card for assistance or see the customer service desk on the first floor to handle my account inquiries. I shake my head in frustration and pull out another credit card which is also declined. This card should also have a great deal of credit available. Now I'm really confused. "I'm sorry," I apologize, utterly embarrassed. "I don't know what's going on." I pull out my debit card and am grateful when it works. Edna bags up my items and I immediately head to the customer service desk to talk to an account representative.

There's no one in line when I arrive to the customer service area so I walk up to the first representative I see. She is a young woman with a warm smile and sunny disposition.

I hand her my card and introduce myself. "Hi. I'm Hope McKinley. I tried to use my card a few minutes ago and the card was declined. There should be plenty of credit available. Can you tell me what's wrong?"

She runs my card through her reader and brings up my account. Her face furrows and she gives me a grim look. "Actually, Ms. McKinley your account is currently over the limit."

"What?!" I retort in a half scream, half question. "How can that be possible? I haven't shopped here in months. At most there should only be about $200 charged on the card."

She pushes some buttons and scrolls through several screens and finally responds. "I do see that on your last billing statement you had a balance of $159.14."

"Yea. That sounds about right. Soo — why isn't my card working?!" I ask again.

"The purchases that were made last week are actually what put your card over the limit." She says.

"Last week?!? I didn't make any purchases last week! I was ... in a coma last week. I just got out of the hospital yesterday. Those purchases are not mine." I say.

She looks at me with great concern and asks, "Was your card stolen?"

"NO, my card wasn't stolen, it's in your hand! How could it be stolen when it's right there!"

"O, yeah," she says as she looks at my card. "Is it possible that you were the victim of identity theft?"

"Well, I guess so. Where were these purchases made? Can you print out a list of what was bought? Do you have copies of the receipts? The purchaser had to sign a receipt, right?"

She punches a few more buttons and begins to look through screens again. She hits a key and the printer warms up behind her and starts to print. It spits out five pages. She grabs them, takes a highlighter and marks the dates and locations of the purchases. "Here are days that your card was used last week. Tuesday July eighth and Wednesday July ninth. The card was actually used here at this location."

Under each date is a laundry list of purchases. I look over the list. There is enough clothing for four or five people to have a complete wardrobe makeover. Shoes, sandals, sneakers, fancy dresses, casual dresses, men's business casual work pants, shirts, and blazers. A couple pages in I come across a green formal gown and Spanx in my size, presumably the funeral dress I just recently took off and the Spanx I'm still wearing. When I scan the shopping spree on day two, I note that practicality went completely out the window. Household furnishings including vases, knick knacks, artwork, and a bedroom suite made the list. I could literally feel my blood pressure going through the roof.

I ask for a copy of the signed receipt. I'm pretty sure of what I'll find but want to see it with my own eyes anyway. She looks through a few more screens and finally comes across the actual receipt copies. A few keystrokes and the receipts print out. When you spend a lifetime growing up with someone, you learn his handwriting pretty well. Although it was my name that was signed, it was definitely my brother's handwriting at the bottom of the receipts.

"Do you want to talk to the fraud department? I can get them on the line for you?"

"Not right now," I answer, obviously deflated. "I'm a little pressed for time. I'll call from home later tonight. Tell me something, can I use these receipt copies to make returns or does it have to be the original?"

"Since these are store printouts, you'll be able to use them." She says. I take the copies, fold them in half and put them in my purse. As I stand to grab my purchases and leave she asks, "Is there anything else I can help you with?"

"No, that's all for now. Thank you."

I walk through the store and take the exit closest to my car. I throw my purchases in the trunk and speed off in complete shock. *Who uses a dead person's credit cards? How tacky can you be?* I'm livid. My phone rings and it's a number I don't recognize. *UGH! I bet it's the taxi driver.* I decline the call and head to an ATM. Three hundred dollars should get me through the next day or so until I can figure out my credit situation. I check my balance and thankfully my checking and savings accounts are intact. Tomorrow I can go to an actual branch and take out more.

I call the number back. As soon as the taxi driver picks up he is yelling and screaming. I sit silently while he rants. When he realizes he hasn't gotten a response he finally pauses and says, "Hello?"

I respond with syrup dripping from my voice. "Hi, this is Hope. You picked me up from the hospital yesterday. Do you remember me?"

He slowly responds, "Yes."

I continue, "I still owe you $25. Do you want to meet somewhere so I can pay you the rest of the money?"

"Ok," he says.

We agree to meet in 20 minutes at Bullshead Pavilion, a small shopping plaza down the street from my apartment. I arrive a few minutes before he does. When I see a taxi start circling the parking lot, I honk my horn and get out of my car so he can see me. He drives over and before he can even speak, I shove $40 through his window and thank him for his patience. I hop back in my car and drive off.

I run to CVS to get some toiletries, my prescriptions, and some much needed wine. I pick up some Wonton soup and fried rice from my favorite Chinese restaurant. Once home, I take a nice, hot bath. It is heaven to be able to lotion my whole body and put on normal undergarments as opposed to the Spanx onesie which is effective but too restrictive for day to day activities. I throw the t-shirt back on and stand at the bar ledge with the bottle of wine, my take out, and my purse. *Crap! I forgot to buy drinking glasses.* Well, at least I chose a bottle of wine with a twist off cap. Drinking from the bottle isn't the least civilized thing I've ever done. Considering my week, it's totally justified. As I eat my fried rice and swig from the wine bottle like a full-fledged alcoholic, I pull out all my credit cards and start making the numerous calls to customer service departments.

I've got four credit cards total. The store credit card has already been addressed so I set that aside. I pull out my Master-Card, the second card to be declined while I was shopping, and call the number on the back. This conversation is virtually a repeat of what happened at Macy's. I ask about purchases in the past week. This card was used to pay for, among other things, my repast. How original. Neither the community center nor the caterers recognized that the dead person's card was being used to pay for their own services. I take down the number to their fraud department in case I need it later.

When I call Best Buy, they tell me which location was visited (one less than 6 miles from my brother's home) and the items purchased. A top of the line car audio/stereo system complete with a back up camera and navigation system was installed the day before the funeral. A kitchen set including a stainless steel refrigerator, stove, and dishwasher were delivered yesterday. An in-home theatre system is scheduled to be installed tomorrow. That maxed out the Best Buy credit card. I cancel tomorrow's installation and ask for an email summary and the number to their fraud department.

The last call to American Express provides a sigh of relief. It hasn't been used. I guess everybody knows not to mess with American Express. Where most companies will end up discharging a claim, American Express will relentlessly pursue and prosecute.

That leaves me with one credit card and my debit card to use. Good to know. It's likely the only reason I still have money in the bank is because my debit card is customized with my picture on it. Hard to use that without risking questions being asked. I also don't have my PIN written down anywhere. Thank God for small blessings. I place the three maxed out cards in one of the kitchen drawers and finish my dinner. I throw on my jeans and decide to head to the local Starbucks. No sense sitting around an empty apartment. I grab a coconut latte something or other and take a seat by the picture window. This is as good a time as any to check all my messages.

Chapter 7

I start with the text messages. A couple from my coworkers last Monday ask where I am. They started to worry when I didn't show up for work. Another message is from an old classmate confirming our plans for happy hour Monday night. Starting on Tuesday, condolences stream in. *Why in the world would someone text the dead person RIP messages??* I shake my head and chuckle to myself. *Well, it's nice someone cared enough to send a message at all, I guess.* Several messages express disbelief including one from Michael, an acquaintance I talk to occasionally:

> Hey HAM - I heard you died. Is it true? Give me a call!

Ummm. That's not how it usually works. *I wonder what he'd do if I call him right now. Freak out?* I start to dial his number but decide that's not a conversation I want to have while sitting in Starbucks.

I read through a few more text messages. One from Emma, an old coworker, melts my heart:

> To HAM's fam. My sincerest condolences. HAM
> was really sweet and I hate to hear the news.
> I always wished we'd had the opportunity
> to get closer. She seemed like a cool chick.
> We always think we have more time than we
> actually do.

Awww. Such sweet words.

As I continue reading, the text messages drastically shift from RIP to WTF. When the messages turn angry I snap to attention:

> WHOEVER POSTED THAT MESSAGE ON
> FACEBOOK U SICK!! THAT SHIT AINT FUNNY!

Facebook? What message? I stop checking texts and quickly open my Facebook app. That's when I see it:

Hope McKinley
July 11 · 🌐 ▾

Hey yall. This is not a joke. I repeat - this is not a joke. I am alive and halfway well. Them fuckers down at "we don't know live people when we see them" funeral homes got me all fucked up. They said I was dead when I really wasn't. Sorry for the inconvenience of anyone who came to my first funeral. I appreciate your support, it was just a bit too early. Stay tuned for more posts in the near future once I straighten this shit out.

Signed,

Management

Oh yeah, THAT message. Jesus, what was I thinking?!? The message I posted while I was in the hospital reached far and wide. Over 3.2K Facebook users posted a comment. It's been shared more than twice that amount from my page alone. Who knows how much further it reached from other people's screenshots and shares. Most of the comments are to the tune of 'WTFs' and 'Is this a joke?' Duh! This wasn't a joke. I even put that in the first line of my post - 'this is not a joke!' All I can do is shake my head.

I scroll through about 100 comments but stop cold when I come to one that has a link to a YouTube video embedded in it. The comment caption asks, 'HAM is this you??' Normally I ignore these types of messages when they pop up in my Messenger app. This is different. Although the preview is a very tiny picture, I can clearly see that it does indeed look like me sitting in a casket wearing a familiar green dress with a panicked look on my face.

My entire body instantly fills with dread. "Please, God, no," I quietly pray under my breath. Although I don't want to do it, I hesitantly tap play. When I do, the scene is more chaotic than anything I could have dreamed. Whoever filmed it had an aisle seat in the fourth row with a clear view of the tacky wooden casket. The amateur videographer instinctively started filming when the casket started to shake.

The scene opens with the pastor running off the pulpit in a complete panic. The casket rocks back and forth causing several attendees to scream. A few people make an early exit.

Just as the lid begins to open, the video abruptly pauses and an ad for **1-800-Flowers** begins to play. For a second I'm dumbfounded. Then, I'm horrified. You have to have A LOT of views to get YouTube ads on your videos. I glance at the information section and see that this video has over six million views. My stomach tightens in knots.

After the brief advertisement the video continues. The lid opens completely. I sit up, and all hell breaks loose with lots of screaming and a mass exodus. Those who don't move fast enough are jumped over. Aunt Fannie's wheelchair gets knocked over almost immediately as people rush toward the exit. She hits her head on the pew right in front of the cameraman. Instead of putting the camera down and rendering aid, a steady hand zooms the camera in for a close up of her injuries. When the camera pans back out, the stampede is over and all that remains is the aftermath of the chaos. The footage doesn't show Cousin Theo getting trampled, but his prosthetic leg is laying in the middle of the aisle. A woman in a white suit approaches the casket from the left side of the chapel. Just as she gets to the casket's edge, the video pauses again and another ad appears. This time it's an ad for **Shea Moisture Hair Products**.

When this ad ends, the woman's head instantly jerks back. I realize this is when I slapped her and I involuntarily let out a loud cackle. The couple sitting next to me break their conversation and give me an awkward glance. I compose myself and go back to viewing the video. The woman is already gone out of the frame by the time I look back at the screen. Not long after she leaves, a plump, dark-skinned guy comes over to me. We have a brief, heated discussion and then he quickly leaves my side.

The final two minutes show me trying in vain to get out of the casket, my mother gasping for air in the front row, and the paramedics rushing in to tend to everyone with serious injuries. The footage ends abruptly when a police officer steps in front of the camera and commands the videographer to leave the chapel.

The moment my life turned upside down is laid out in a 17 minute and fifty-two second YouTube video ... with two sponsors. When Brandon described the chaos, I yearned for a YouTube video. Now that I've seen it, along with millions of others, I sit in disbelief as tears stream down my face. I look around the cafe wondering how many in this room have watched it. No one seems to be staring in my direction so I take that as a good sign. Still, I feel a sense of shame. With so many views in just two days, it seems like everyone in the world has seen it.

I return my attention to my phone and tap the arrow to display the comments. The good news is initially many people thought this was movie footage that didn't make the final cut. It didn't take long, though, for people hellbent on being important to chime in with their two cents. Those who were in attendance gave their firsthand accounts. Links to my obituary were placed in the comments so those not in attendance could verify that this was indeed a real funeral service.

I want to comment or at least make another Facebook post but am too stunned to think of what to say. Instead I close the app and set my phone down. I really just want to go home where I can curl up into a ball and cry but it's too early. I need to give my family enough time to return my belongings and be gone by the time I get back home. I'm not up for seeing anyone right now. I order another coconut drink and spend the next few hours wading through emails.

Long after nightfall I make my way home. When I open the door I'm immediately taken aback. Boxes are piled high all over the place with my furniture haphazardly placed in the living and dining room. I walk inside, shut the door, and lean against it completely overwhelmed. I don't have the energy to start looking through boxes. I head to the bedroom and am thankful to find the bed set up. I crawl into it, curl up in the covers, and drift into a restless sleep.

Chapter 8

Monday, July 14, 2014

After tossing and turning all night I decide to get up when shades of blue-gray start peeking through the window. It feels nice to be back in my own bed but I still can't seem to sleep for long stretches of time. My entire apartment is in disarray which makes it hard to focus. I'm not looking forward to today at all. Figuratively and literally, I have to unravel the mess that is my life. I know this is not going to be easy.

I don't have any of my important papers handy so I fire up my laptop and go to the city's employee portal to access my benefit information. Our life insurance company's contact information is hyperlinked making it easy for me to dial the number. After a few prompts asking for identifying information, I'm connected to a perky agent named Paula in the claims department.

"Hi Paula, this is Hope McKinley. I have a policy through your company. I need to check the status of my benefits."

"I'm sorry Ms. McKinley, you've reached the claims department. You need customer service. Hold a moment and I'll be happy to connect you —"

"NO, wait. I actually do want the claims department. I want to check and see if a claim has been filed on my policy."

Silence on the other end of the line. Finally she says, "I'm not sure I understand." This is a phrase I'm quickly becoming accustomed to.

I give a brief overview of the mis-declaration of death and ask if the funeral home filed a claim against my policy. More silence on her end. "Do you need my social security number to look up the policy?"

"Yeah, sure," she replies. Confusion replaces her once chipper tone. She keys in the information and after a slight pause confirms, "Yes, there is a claim filed for this insurance policy." The policy is for $100,000. Turns out the funeral expenses were billed for just under $24,000. Based on what I saw when I woke up I can't imagine what the money was spent on. The casket couldn't have been more than a few hundred bucks. Where in the world did the rest of the money go? Since none of that is her problem, I set those feelings aside and continue.

I ask how to dispute the claim. She has no idea and transfers me to a supervisor. I go through the spiel, again. Big, big mixup. Folks thought I was dead. Funeral home filed a claim. I need to stop payment and reactivate the policy. Again, silence on the other end of the phone. She, too, is clueless on how to handle this one. She takes my contact information and promises to get back to me within a few days. Good. At least there will be a note on my account and the policy likely won't get paid out. The last thing I want to do is chase folks down to get my money back.

In the shower I consider my next steps. I dry off while browsing through my closet. I'm glad to see my clothes but the closet is so disorganized I can't quickly put an outfit together. Remembering the previous day's visit to the mall I go to the living room to find my shopping bag. I decide on the sexy red dress for today's battle. It's a gorgeous, slinky number that hugs every curve. After some searching I find silver shoes, a silver handbag, and matching jewelry. A pop of red lipstick and off I go.

* * * *

I pull into the funeral home parking lot around 9:30AM. One last check in the rearview mirror and I head inside. An appropriately somber funeral attendant complete with lavender suit, kitten heels, and matching church hat greets me at the door. She introduces herself as Lucinda, Cin for short, and asks how she can be of assistance. I look at her inquisitively. She has no idea who I am. That's interesting.

I start my script, "My dear father passed away suddenly

56

last night. I asked around for referrals and was told that this funeral home is the best. Daddy was a pastor and must be laid to rest in a respectful, dignified manner. Money is no object. I want to work with Mr. and Mrs. Johnson directly. Are they in, I'd like to discuss what services they can provide."

"Certainly Ms. ...?" Her question lingers.

"Nora. Just call me Nora." I lie.

"Yes, Ms. Nora. I'll get Mr. & Mrs. Johnson for you. Please, make yourself comfortable."

I sit down on one of the plush round sofas set in the middle of the lobby. Cin disappears briefly and comes back to announce, "Mrs. Johnson stepped out to visit with a family. Mr. Johnson is finishing up a call and will be right down. Can I get you some water, coke, or orange juice while you wait?" I politely decline the offer.

As I look around the waiting area, movement upstairs catches my eye. I glance up to see Mr. Johnson positioned at the top of the staircase like a bride about to make her grand entrance. Gray tailor-made suit. Burnt orange dress shirt. Perfectly matching gray and orange paisley tie. Freshly done haircut and mustache shaping. He probably has someone come in every couple of days to do his hair in the office. I resist the urge to roll my eyes and scoff. My brain is spinning. I can't WAIT to knock him off his pedestal. But I have to play it cool, for now.

After giving me enough time to take in all his splendor, Mr. Johnson finally glides down the curved staircase. I am angry and disgusted, but I hope the look on my face doesn't betray me. I try to look like a grieving next of kin as he approaches. He extends his hand and I stand to greet him. He leads me down the same long hallway Cin disappeared down earlier. We come to an arched French doorway. He opens the door with a flourish and allows me to step inside first. This room is obviously where the money is made. Beautiful casket samples, casket liners, and urns frame the room, Memorial keepsakes of picture frames, knickknacks, and teddy bears pepper the focal wall. On the table are catalogs of more casket selections, floral arrangements, and keepsake items. I take a seat closest to the door. As I look around I can't help but notice there are a lot of nicer choices than what was chosen for me. I have to remind myself to stay focused.

Mr. Johnson closes the door and sits next to me. He moves the catalogs closer. Magically a box of tissues appear in front of me. Inwardly I smile and think, *Oh, I'm not the one who'll need tissues by the end of this meeting.* He's clearly the king of the funeral sales pitch. Little does he know today is not going to be his lucky day.

He arranges some forms to take notes on and then turns to me. "My assistant tells me you've just lost your father. Please allow me to extend my sincerest condolences. I am so very sorry for your loss." His voice is rich and deep. His almond-shaped eyes have a warmth and depth that can easily make you forget he's acting. Over the years he's perfected the look of solemnity that he expresses in this moment as he reaches to tenderly hold my hand and caress my arm.

I sit in silence for a few seconds. Then I look at him with a confused look on my face, "There's nothing wrong with my father. He's alive and well."

Now *he* looks confused. "I'm sorry. I must have misunderstood. Ms. Nora … who are you here to make arrangements for?"

I pause. "Hmm. I don't look familiar to you?" When he doesn't answer I continue, "I suppose I do look a lot different when I'm not in a casket."

His facial expression has gone from solemn, to confused, to a glimmer of Oh Shit! He's starting to get it.

"That's right, Mr. Johnson. My name isn't Nora. My name is Hope McKinley, and you and your staff tried to bury me last week."

The moment I've been dreaming of ever since I saw his online profile is finally here. A look of sheer panic crosses his face. It looks divine. He snatches his hand from my arm and pushes back in his chair, nearly knocking himself over. I grab my phone and quickly snap a few pictures.

I watch his contorted face change from understanding to horror to pure fear. All that confidence and swag he had at the top of the staircase is long gone. When he tries to bolt for the door I push my chair back, effectively blocking his exit.

With no way to escape he does the unexpected. He throws up all over himself and starts clutching his chest. Now it's time for my Oh Shit moment. *Oh my God! Is he having a heart attack?* I hadn't anticipated THAT!

I dart out the room and scream for help. Cin comes running out the back office, run being a generous term. I scream, "Call an ambulance, I think Mr. Johnson is having a heart attack!"

Cin cries, "Oo my dear Lord!! Jay, Martha! Come quick, it's an emergency!!" A few more people race into the sales room. Cin disappears back into her office, presumably to call an ambulance. I hear prayers and pleas coming from the sales room. With all the confusion I slip out unnoticed. I rush to my car and hightail it out of there. A few miles down the road I pull into the parking lot of a crowded plaza.

Shit! Shit! Shit! How could this happen? Wasn't he expecting me to eventually pay him a visit! Did he think I would just let 'trying to bury me alive' go? As I sit in my car mentally beating myself up, an ambulance speeds by going in the direction of the funeral home. "FUCK!" I grab the steering wheel and rest my head on the backs of my hands.

After a long while I hear taps on my window. When I jerk my head up I see an officer staring at me with a concerned look on his face. I crack the window a few inches. "Ma'am, are you ok? Someone reported a suspicious person sleeping in their car."

"I'm fine officer, just deep in thought. I guess I lost track of time."

"All right. Just checking on you."

"Thank you. I appreciate that," I reply. I watch him walk away, then I put the car in reverse and slowly ease out of my parking space. I exit the lot, pull out into the street, and head away from the funeral home.

Not wanting to go home and sit amongst the sea of boxes, I drive a few miles down the road and pull into a local pub. I just want to relax with some comfort food and a good stiff cocktail. After the week I've had, I more than deserve it. Thank goodness the bar isn't crowded. I choose a booth with a good view of the tv screens away from the two guys at the bar.

The bar waitress is an elderly blonde with her hair pulled back in a long, curly ponytail. Wearing tight faded black jeans, black patent leather sneakers, a tank top, and a plaid shirt tied in a knot around her waist, she looks a mess but is sweet as pie when she comes over to take my order. I order my usual - buffalo wings extra crispy, as spicy as they can get, and a spiced rum and coke. It's been too long since I've had my favorites. The food comes quickly and I scarf it down. I really haven't had much to eat since being released from the hospital two days ago. I pull up my to-do list which by now has been converted to the Notes app on my iPhone. I look at what I've accomplished and what more needs to be done. Not long after pulling up my to-do list, my stomach growls like a tiger is about to attack. Oh, shit! I grab my stomach, shove all my stuff in my purse, and run to the bathroom. I barely make it on the toilet before pure fire shoots out my ass. I bite the leather straps on my purse to keep from screaming and pray no one else comes in. Beads of sweat form on my forehead as my stomach does somersaults. Lesson learned. The first real meal after being dead for a week should NOT be spice, on top of spice, with a spice and coke chaser. UGH!

I sit there panting and sweating for half an hour. Finally my heart rate starts to come back down. I put myself back together as best I can. My day is officially shot to shit. I pay my bill and drag myself home where the toilet bowl and I are besties for the rest of the evening.

Chapter 9

Tuesday, July 15, 2014

I jerk awake. I'm on the bathroom floor curled around the toilet bowl. The apartment is chilly and I'm shivering, but my stomach is calmer and I'm no longer sweating. My ass still burns though. I've never had anal but I imagine this is what the aftermath feels like. There's certainly nothing enticing about this. After slowly making my way to my feet I throw some cleanser on my face and hop in the shower. When I step out I feel like a new person. My stomach is still a bit queasy but I can make it through the day ... going back to a restricted diet of course. I apply face moisturizer, lotion, and deodorant and lie on the bed. When I wake again it's nearly noon.

I decide it's time to deal with the newspaper obituary. I head to the closet and choose a light summer sweater with a side zipper and scooped cowl neck. I pair it with a black skirt and black heels. A tasteful natural makeup job pulls the look together and I'm out the door.

* * * *

The Springfield News headquarters is a five-story brick structure that sits on the corner of Main & 3rd. The garage spans two floors underground. Small businesses occupy floors 1-4. *The Springfield News* takes up the entire 5th floor. At one time it commanded the entire building and served as a thriving employer in this city. The online era whittled this print newspaper down to a shell of itself. I head to their entrance with a copy of my obituary in hand. The front desk clerk cheerily greets, "Welcome to *The Springfield News*. Who are you here to see?"

"I'm here to see whoever handles obituaries."

"Do you need to place a notice? I'm so sorry for your loss."

"Thank you for your condolences but I don't need to place a notice. I actually need a retraction?"

"A ... retraction? From the obit department? I'm not sure I understand."

"Well, let me help you." I unfold the copy of my obituary and hold it to her face. "Does the person in this obituary look familiar to you? This is MY obituary. Obviously, I don't need one yet. This ran in your paper last week and I need a retraction! Do you understand now?"

She turns ashen gray like she's just seen a ghost. Sadly, I'm starting to get used to that look. Her perfect red lips freeze in an "o" and she sits there stunned, seemingly unable to move. I snap my fingers and she jerks like she is awakening from a hypnotic spell.

"I think you were about to call someone for me, from the obit department." She shakes the cobwebs from her head and nervously picks up the phone.

Poor thing can barely hold the receiver in her hands. She punches in three digits and turns her back to me as she has a quiet conversation with whoever is on the other end. She turns again to briefly address me. "Excuse me, what is your name?"

"Hope McKinley," I say, as I thrust the obituary back in her face so she can read it for herself.

The little color she'd regained leaves her face and she turns back around to finish her conversation. She hangs up the phone and quietly says, "Ben Thompson is our obit editor. He'll be with you in a few moments. Please have a seat."

I sit in the sparsely decorated lobby. I'm moody but I take a few deep breaths to calm myself down before Ben arrives. Fifteen minutes pass before a bulky, disheveled gentleman timidly approaches. "Ms. McKinley?" I stand and extend my hand. "Yes, I'm Hope McKinley." He doesn't immediately shake my hand but once he realizes I'm not moving until he does, he has no choice and relents. He offers a wimpy handshake and leads me to a small conference room just off the lobby where he motions to a seat and shuts the door. He begins to sweat and I can tell he's dreading this meeting. I can't blame him.

Ben sits across from me and reluctantly dives in. "Ms. McKinley, I'm confused as to what's going on here. Amanda tells me that we ran your obituary last week. Help me understand how this is possible. Was someone playing a joke on you?"

"No," I say in a half laugh, half sigh. "No one was playing a joke on me. Unfortunately everyone actually thought I was dead." I repeat my story yet again, ending with my waking up in a casket to the dismay of all the attendees. I show him the copies of the general obit run in the newspaper, and the more robust profile posted on the funeral home's website. "As you can see, I don't need these quite yet. I need a retraction."

"Ms. McKinley, to run a retraction in the obit section is highly unusual, as I'm sure you can imagine. A good portion of our subscribers are avid readers of the obit section. To pull back a death notice would make us seem incompetent at best and would certainly confuse the readers."

"Your reputation is not my problem. The fact is, I'm not dead and everyone who thought that I was needs to be informed. No one is going to blame *you*. You didn't try to bury a live body, but you did run an inaccurate story and that needs to be corrected.

"How about this?" I offer. "Instead of just a brief two-line retraction that leaves people with more questions than answers, how about an entire story. An exposé on the incompetencies of the city morgue and the Johnson Family Funeral Homes. I don't know how they did what they did, but this has got to be front page worthy. Above the fold, even. Oh and look at this!" I grab my phone and pull up the photos app. "You can use this as the feature photo of your story."

"What in the world is this?" he asks.

"It's a picture of Mr. Johnson, the funeral home director."

"He looks like he's having a heart attack," Ben looks at the picture with disgust.

"He did!" I exclaim a little too excitedly. Ben aims his disgust at me and I quickly tone it down.

"Ben, this could be the biggest story of your career. Think of how explosive this could be; and the public has a right to know this is possible, especially anyone who hires the Johnson Family Funeral Homes to bury their loved ones. They need to beware."

"Ms. McKinley ..."

"Please, call me Hope," I interrupt.

"OK, Hope - this is a rare occasion. It's not like there's really a chance that this will happen on a regular basis. There is really nothing to beware *of.* "

I sit back in my chair. "You're afraid of this story. Maybe it's too big for you. You do small obit ads for the oldies who read your section every day and just thank God THEIR name isn't in there. Maybe this story would be better suited for John Goldstein. He's always got a story on the front page. I'm sure he'd jump right on this. Where's his office?" I pop out of my chair and reach for my purse.

"No wait! Just let me think about this for a minute."

"I'll give you thirty seconds before I head out to the lobby and have Amanda call someone who's interested in what I'm offering, You know John Goldstein would be all over this."

Ben absentmindedly narrows his eyes and starts to chew on his bottom lip. I've hit a nerve. Apparently there's no love lost between those two.

"OK, ok. I'll run the story, but I don't want it to be scandalous. If I'm going to write a story, I want it to be one of value. Something of substance that will truly help the public."

"Ah, that's so noble of you. Not the typical attitude of a journalist. No wonder you're stuck in obits." He slumps slightly. I bend down so we're face to face. "You write all the substance you want. Just make sure to get all the details in there, and use this picture. Where do you want me to send it?" He sighs and gives me his email address. I send the picture immediately. "The story will be running in tomorrow's newspaper."

"I'll have to talk to the editor and see …," he tries to stall.

I immediately cut him off, "That wasn't a question!" I grab my purse and head toward the conference room door. "I'll be grabbing a copy of *The Springfield News* first thing in the morning, Ben." With that I saunter across the lobby and out the door.

* * * *

The next morning I hop out of bed and hurry down to the 7-11 to grab a copy of the newspaper. My story *is* on the front page above the fold, but it's in a small column on the left side of the paper. Eight short lines fit in that little column and the rest of the article is buried in the back of the newspaper on page 2H, the second page of the obit section.

At the very top of 2H is a split picture. The picture used in my original obituary is on the left, the picture of Frederick Johnson, Jr. at the onset of a heart attack is on the right. His picture looks even more unflattering and gruesome in black and white. Secretly I love it. The Johnsons will suffer the same way I have. The text of the article reads:

> A common phrase states that there is a first time for everything. Today we experienced what is certainly a first for us at The Springfield News.
>
> You may recall that we ran an obituary notification on July 9th, 2014 - July 10th, 2014 announcing the death of Hope Allison McKinley. We are pleased to report that Ms. McKinley is actually alive. Many of you may be thinking what I initially thought. Certainly, someone must have played a cruel joke. I can assure you that is not the case.
>
> On Monday, July 7th, 2014 the Medical Examiner's Office mistakenly declared Ms.

McKinley deceased and allowed her body to
be retrieved by The Johnson Family Funeral
Homes. The funeral home staff failed to do
a proper evaluation of Ms. McKinley and
proceeded to perform funeral services.
Thankfully, Ms. McKinley had the good fortune
to wake from her coma prior to experiencing
any long-term consequences.

The Springfield News reached out to both the
Medical Examiner's Office and The Johnson
Family Funeral Homes. No comment was
provided at the time this article went to print.

The Springfield News would like to offer Ms.
Hope McKinley our sincerest well wishes as
she moves forward with what we hope is a
long and prosperous life.

Eh. It's not as colorful as I'd hoped for but I have to give
the benefit of the doubt. Ben is used to regurgitating four-
line obits from information on a pre-filled form. I'm sure this
was far beyond his comfort zone. I grab a coffee to go with
the paper and head back home to start the day.

I pick out a nice pastel pink summer dress and spend a little
extra time on my hair and makeup. Now that the retraction is
printed I feel people need to hear something directly from me.
I decide to record a quick Facebook live so people can see and

hear that I'm ok. I walk to the pool area and use the waterfall as a backdrop for my video update:

> "Hey Y'all. It's HAM. As most of you have probably realized by now, this is NOT a joke. I really am alive. I don't even know where to begin. If you've talked to my family or read *The Springfield News* article that ran today, then you have some idea of what happened. I don't have much to add beyond that. I'm still in the process of unraveling this entire mess. Just know that I'm recuperating and straightening things out and will be in touch with those of you closest to me real soon. Thank you for all the messages of well wishes and concern. I truly appreciate those of you who have sent notes of support during this crazy time. Ta Ta For Now."

There. Short, sweet, and hopefully endearing. This will at least let my friends know I'm ok. I finish the video and make sure it uploads before I log out. There are hundreds of notifications and messages on my account but I just can't bear to deal with them right now.

Part Two

Chapter 10

Two weeks after the funeral

For someone who's not actually dead, I'm spending a lot of time in a funeral home. I arrive around 10:00AM. When she hears the door, Cin comes quickly down the hall until she sees who it is. She loses a bit of pep when she recognizes me. I have a smile plastered on my face that will not crack. When she gets a few feet from me I speak first. "Hi, Cin! How are you? And how is Mr. Johnson? The last time I saw him he didn't look so good." She has as much ice in her facial expression as I have sarcastic smirk in mine. I see she's not going to answer so I continue. "Who's in charge of billing? There's a little matter I need to discuss," I ask as I wave a billing statement in front of her face. She glances at the document, turns on her heels and heads down the hall. After a few minutes of seeing and hearing no one, I take a seat on one of the ostentatious round sofas, frowning in displeasure as I wait.

Finally, a woman casually dressed in olive green slacks, an untucked white silk-like blouse, and black rundown flats comes down the hallway. Clearly, she doesn't normally see clients. She asks uneasily what she can do for me. I show her the bill I received in the mail and say, "I think there's been some kind of mistake."

"About the bill? Let me take a look," she says.

"Actually, is there somewhere we can talk in private?" I eye another family who is also waiting in the lobby. She walks me to the same salesroom where Mr. Johnson had his heart attack and I take the same seat closest to the door. She sits where he originally sat and I lay the billing statement on the table.

She picks it up and asks what the issue is. "I'd like to know why I got a bill in the mail for a funeral I didn't need," I respond. I fully expect her to apologize for the obvious error. To my surprise, she actually tries to rationalize this bullshit.

"Well, I understand your question," she starts. "Let me try to clarify the statement for you." My face pulls into a near grimace as she starts to break down the bill. "We recently received a notice from the insurance company that they denied our claim. That is why we had to forward the final bill to you, it hasn't been covered."

"It hasn't been covered, because it's not necessary," I fume, failing to conceal my contempt. "Why the hell would I pay for flowers, a chapel, and a casket that I don't need?"

"Well, to be fair we didn't charge you the full price of the casket. We reduced it to our rental fee since it was not used to completion."

"Excuse me?!?" I push my purse aside and lean in close to face her. I didn't even realize I was moving until she slowly started to retreat. Despite my obvious growing anger, she continues.

"Since you didn't take ownership of the casket, we felt wrong charging the full fee; but we cant re-market it as a new casket. It's been used, the value has been reduced. So as a compromise, we've charged you our casket rental fee which is just under half of the full market cost. Our rental fees are a steal really."

It takes everything in me not to jump out of my seat and choke the shit out of her. "Your rental fees are a steal for people who actually need a casket. I. NEVER. NEEDED. IT!" I slam my hand on the table.

She jumps and quickly slides her chair back.

I massage my temples in an attempt to calm down. It would be a cruel twist of fate to have a heart attack in the same spot Mr. Johnson did. I've already been carted out of this establishment once. I have no desire to leave here on a stretcher again. Who knows if these people would even render me any assistance. I snatch up the billing statement and leave without another word. I don't know why I haven't thought of it until now, but it's time for me to find an attorney.

Chapter 11

I head to the car and immediately start searching for attorneys. I'm not even sure what I need. The ads for criminal attorneys dominate my search. I came close to choking the life out of the funeral home's billing agent, but thankfully I restrained myself so a criminal attorney isn't needed right now. There's also plenty of ads for wrongful death attorneys but that doesn't seem quite right either. I was wrongfully *declared* dead, but since I'm not *actually* dead I don't think they can help. Then, ads for trial attorneys catch my eye. After scanning websites for a few minutes I decide to give Walsh & Edelman a call. I've seen their commercials and absentmindedly pass by their office building all the time. They seem prosperous which must mean they are great at what they do. That being said, I expect to get an appointment in a week or so. I press the hyperlink that autodials their number. A merry receptionist answers the phone, "Thank you for calling Walsh & Edelman. This is Sarah. How may I direct your call?"

"Hi Sarah. My name is Hope McKinley. I need to make an appointment to speak with someone regarding a legal matter. I'm not really sure who I need to speak to, but I need to sue a funeral home."

When she puts me on hold I assume it's to check a scheduling calendar. I'm shocked when she quickly returns and informs me I can be seen today if I have the time. "Sure, I'm only about half an hour away. Does that work?" I reply.

"Absolutely! Do you know where our office is?"

"Yes. Doesn't everyone?" I chuckle.

She laughs back. "Yes, I guess our building is hard to miss. When you arrive, our firm is on the top three floors. Reception is located on floor 20. Just come on in and I'll be at the front desk to greet you. We look forward to meeting you."

"Sounds great, see you soon." I hang up and excitedly drive over to their office.

The building is a massive structure just off the expressway. At 23 stories, it's one of the tallest in the city and stands alone in the skyline. It's been in the running for architectural awards for its spiral cone design. Although it's seen a great deal of critical acclaim, most people just think it looks like a giant penis. I arrive around lunchtime and thankfully find quite a few parking spaces in the lot close to the main entrance. I grab one and head up to the twentieth floor.

As I step off the elevator a middle age man is angrily screaming at the receptionist, "This is bullshit! I scheduled this appointment a month ago!" He blows past me and hops in the elevator I stepped out of before the doors finish closing. I walk up to the reception desk and inquire, "Is everything ok?" Sarah greets me warmly. "Yes, everything is fine. We just had to reschedule his appointment. Are you Miss McKinley?"

"Yes, I am."

"Great! I'm glad you could make it in. Please have a seat and we'll call you back shortly."

A few minutes go by before a stout man in his mid-50s with black hair and a fitted gray suit approaches me. He extends a hand and warmly says, "Miss McKinley. My name is Steve Edelman. Thank you for coming in."

He leads me to a conference room where a dashing gentleman is standing behind a chair at the head of a six seater table. Standing tall, slim, handsome, with salt and pepper hair and a tailor-made navy suit, he is Steve's opposite. He offers a firm handshake as Steve makes the introduction. "Ms. McKinley, this is Theodore Walsh, our founding partner."

"Ms. McKinley, it's a pleasure to meet you. Please have a seat," he greets as he pulls out the head chair for me.

"Can I interest you in some refreshments?" Mr. Edelman asks as he points to a spread on the table. As a centerpiece there's a silver platter with grapes, strawberries, crackers, and an assortment of cheeses. Small saucers are placed off to the side. It almost looks like the makings of a romantic picnic. Not at all what I expected but I appreciate the offer.

"Sure," I respond as I arrange cheese, crackers, and grapes on a small plate.

"What can I pour you to drink?" Mr. Edelman asks as he heads to an impressively stocked wet bar. I glance over the selections and request a Chardonnay and bottled water.

Steve serves my beverages. The two attorneys sit on either side of the table as a screen silently descends covering the wall directly in front of me.

Mr. Walsh gives me an overview of the law firm as a perfectly timed powerpoint presentation runs to his narration. An impressive trial record of high profile cases is displayed and they are chomping at the bit to add mine to their list. Although it should probably unnerve me, it gives me comfort to know they've discussed my situation at great length and have already outlined issues to investigate and possibly litigate. At the top of the list is the funeral home. Also included is an investigation of city morgue procedures to determine how things got this far. After a 45-minute discussion we hash out a plan of action. I hand over the billing statement from the funeral home. My life insurance documents are easily accessible on the city's employee portal. I email those over. I promise to forward my credit card statements within the week. They have me fill out a HIPAA release form so they can access my hospital records with my diagnosis and follow up regimen.

I leave feeling like a weight is lifted off my shoulders. I no longer have to bear the heavy lifting of this complex investigation on my own.

Chapter 12

Two months after the funeral

In the months since "the incident" I've had a horrible case of insomnia. I'm in a constant state of anxiety and panic. Eventually I returned to work but haven't been able to focus. I routinely snap at my coworkers. On top of everything else, the relationship with my family has gotten increasingly tense. Everyone means well, but no one knows what to say or do so they generally avoid me. I'm constantly frustrated because I just want normalcy but almost every day someone points at me and says, "Hey, aren't you that dead girl?" How do you come back from that? I have no idea. I just know things can't continue on this way. I decide that it's time I see a psychiatrist. However, I don't want to see AK from the hospital. She looked more like a walking dead girl than I did. I pick up the phone and play Google roulette.

The profile of Ian Washington, M.D. catches my eye. First, he's handsome. Second, the bio says he focuses on anxiety and insomnia, two of my major issues. Third, I appreciate the tagline - 'Professional Counseling With A Christian Perspective.' I don't go to church much but reading this calms my spirit. I screenshot the number so I can call for an appointment during business hours.

* * * *

Although I had to book the session nearly two weeks out, my appointment date seems to arrive quickly. I go to the doctor's office but I'm apprehensive. I've never placed much stock in counseling and don't know anyone who's ever gone. Or, at least no one has ever admitted it to me. There is no receptionist. This is one of those shared office spaces where different professionals appear in the lobby to retrieve the clients they magically know are waiting. I'm the only one in the lobby at the moment so I grab a seat in the modestly decorated space. Pretty much everything is beige with a couple of muted paintings on the wall. A coffee table holds a variety of magazines to help those waiting pass the time. About five minutes before my scheduled appointment time, a tall, dark, well-groomed gentleman comes to greet me. He looks exactly like his picture.

Dr. Washington walks over to me and extends his hand. "Ms. McKinley?"

"Yep. That's me." I shake his hand and try to sound cheerful but I'm sure my facial expression betrays me. It always does.

"Great! If you're ready, please follow me back to my office." He leads me through a series of hallways. On the way to his office we pass various businesses - attorneys, insurance agents, and consultants mostly. At the back of the building we enter a small office beautifully decorated in earth tones. Electric candles provide dimmed lighting. In the back corner of the room a small water fountain creates soothing background noise. Dr. Washington's desk and office chair are set against the wall next to the doorway. A soft leather sofa and fabric loveseat await his clients. Decorative vases and a box of tissues rest on a beautiful wood coffee table. A comfy teal and brown chenille blanket is strewn across the sofa. I sit on a corner of the sofa. He sits at his desk with a notepad and begins.

"Thank you for coming in today. I'm very passionate about mental health and am always encouraged when a new patient decides to take control of life by seeking professional guidance. I read over the new patient forms you filled out online. So, this is your first time seeing a psychiatrist?" he turns to me inquisitively.

"Yes, that's correct," I confirm.

"And I see that you have concerns about depression, anxiety, and insomnia. Are these recent or have you been struggling for a while?"

"They're pretty recent. I'm not sure if you're being modest or if you honestly don't recognize me from all the media, but I'm the woman who woke up at my own funeral." I pull out a copy of the obituary and retraction article for him to review. "Over the past couple months I've been trying to put my life back together. I thought when I got all the pieces in place things would get better. It's taking a lot longer than I expected to get back on track. In the meantime things just keep getting worse."

"What do you mean by that? What happened that did not meet your expectations?" He prods gently.

"Well, I still have a place to live, I was finally able to get a handle on all my credit cards, and my finances are intact. My immediate needs are met, which is great. But as far as relationships go, everything just feels different. My relationships with my coworkers and family are strained. I can't explain it. I feel like an outsider in my own life and I hate it." I start to tear up and reach for a tissue. He remains silent for a few seconds to let me recover.

"Have you experienced any physiological changes since the incident? You mentioned insomnia. Is there anything else?"

"Insomnia is a huge issue. It's very hard for me to go to sleep. It's a struggle every night. I can do short cat naps when I'm absolutely exhausted, but I haven't slept through the night since I woke up in a casket."

"Any nightmares?"

"None that I ever remember, but I often jerk awake as if something scares me in my sleep. Most nights I go to bed with the lights on. Total darkness makes me feel uneasy."

"How's your appetite? Are you getting three balanced meals a day?"

"Not really. I may eat once a day if it crosses my mind. Every now and then I may snack on something but, I just don't have an appetite."

He jots some notes then asks, "What about your mood? Have you seen any changes in that?"

"I'm sure my coworkers would say there are changes," I say with a quiet laugh. "I'm just a lot less tolerant of ... everything. I feel like everyone at work has discussed my situation behind my back and I don't know what they feel or what they think. A few people try to invite me out, but I just feel like I'm the joke of the party so I normally turn them down. And my family is so distant. It's like no one knows what to say or do. It's frustrating." More tears and tissues.

"I don't know what to do. There's no support group that I can attend. No one has been in this position before. Sure people have died, had CPR performed on them, and been brought back to life. But to be declared dead. Morgue, funeral home, all of it. Then pop back to life again. To my knowledge, no one's been through THAT. And for once, I'm not proud to be the first at something. I don't know where to go from here. But I do know that if someone points at me one more time and says, 'Hey aren't you that dead girl?' I'm going to lose it. Every day there is a new struggle. I'm frustrated and exhausted and I can't even sleep." Although

I'm sobbing at this point, I feel better now that I've gotten all that off my chest.

"Since you touched on it a little bit, what *do* you do to cope?"

"I guess I don't," I say tearfully.

"Have you noticed any increase in dependance on substances, like smoking or alcohol perhaps?"

I halt in the middle of wiping away tears. "Are you about to tell me to stop drinking wine? 'Cause if that's your idea of therapy, I'm out."

He stifles a quiet laugh. "Not stop. Minimize. Just so you can stay in tune with your true feelings and process through your experiences with clear judgment." I give him a distrustful glance and he chuckles again. "I promise I'm not taking away your wine." Dr. Washington writes some brief notes and then puts the pen and pad down."

"First, thank you for your openness and honesty. It takes a lot of courage to take this step. Second, everything you feel is normal. You've been through an extraordinary experience. It makes perfect sense that you are having these feelings and reactions. You woke up mere hours from being buried alive. That can be very hard to wrap your mind around. During that week leading up to the funeral, who knows what conversations and events were going on around you that infiltrated your psyche and are causing these responses. And I'm sure the odd reactions you're receiving from family and associates aren't imagined. They probably *don't* know what to say. A lot of their apprehension may stem from care and concern. They don't want to say anything to upset you further so sometimes silence, or distance, is easier. Be gentle with them. Be gentle with yourself. Know that healing is a process. It will take time, probably a lot longer than two months, to regain your footing."

I smile through the tears. Knowing that these feelings are normal puts me at ease. What I really want is for these feelings and mood swings to go away. I respond, "I appreciate everything you've said, but I don't know if I'm up for a lengthy process. I want my life back the way it was before all this happened."

To my chagrin the doctor responds, "I don't know if your life will ever completely go back to the way it was. Your situation was in the paper. It was discussed by the masses. Unfortunately, in our society, when a situation goes viral people aren't quick to forget it. What we have to focus on is establishing a new normal for you."

That news doesn't make me happy but I'm determined to hear his thoughts on establishing this new plan. "So how do I move forward. I can't continue the way things are now."

"I understand. I'm sure the symptoms and experiences you've endured have only added to an already stressful situation. I'm going to throw out a term that you may have heard before and I don't want it to scare you."

"Ok," I say hesitantly.

"You are exhibiting signs of Post Traumatic Stress Disorder, or PTSD. To be quite honest, I'm surprised you're doing as well as you are under the circumstances."

"Isn't PTSD what soldiers get when they go off to war?"

He nods in agreement. "Yes, that is what PTSD is often associated with, but that's not the only event that brings on the disorder. PTSD can be triggered by any stressful event - a bad car accident, a house fire, an abusive relationship. Any severe trauma can trigger this disorder."

Deep sigh. "Ok, so what do we do about it?"

"One-on-one therapy sessions like this are a great start. There are also a few different treatment options that can be tried in addition to traditional counseling. For starters, I can prescribe something to help you sleep. I think you'll see a huge difference in your daily life once you're getting the proper amount of rest."

"Nope. Absolutely not. I am not here for any prescriptions. I don't want chemicals in my body and I certainly don't want anything altering my mind. I'm going to pass on any kind of medication for now."

"OK. I can appreciate that but remember it is an option if you should change your mind. Many find medication very effective and often don't have to be on it longterm. Another option that many people find successful is a therapy dog. You can get one that's been specifically trained to work with PTSD patients, or you can purchase a puppy ..."

He stops talking when he sees me vigorously shaking my head no. "I hate the idea of a dog even more than I hate the idea of medication. When I want to clean up poop for years on end, I'll have a baby. At least, at some point, they grow up and go away."

"Oooh-kaay," he says, a bit more hesitant than he's been this entire conversation. "Well, just to reiterate, those two techniques are very effective in helping patients heal from trauma and manage symptoms. But there are other options. There are several types of support groups that you can try. Support groups are not one size fits all, so you may have to go to a few before you find one that works for you. Sometimes it helps to engage in conversations with others who share your symptoms, even if they don't necessarily share your experience. There are also online support groups and coaches specifically geared towards PTSD.

"As far as things you can try on your own, many find that exercising, meditating, and journaling are quite effective. For you, I would suggest a mood journal. Whenever you feel your mood shift or whenever you start to get agitated, write down what's happening. Who are you talking to? What's the conversation about? How did you react? Over time you may start to see a pattern. That will give us a clear sense of what the trigger points are and exactly what we need to overcome. Does any of that sound doable?"

I pause for a moment to take it all in. "Actually, yes. I don't really want to go to an in-person group thing, but I wouldn't mind the online options you mentioned. I can do the journal too. I never really thought about there being a pattern to my anger. That sounds like a key step to getting over this hurdle."

"Great! I'm glad there are some options that may work for you. How about this ... for your homework why don't you work on your mood journal? You can arrange it any way you want but try to make entries every day. I also want you to go to at least one social gathering in the next week. Maybe you and your family members can get together for dinner or a group activity. Or, you can take your coworkers up on one of their invites. The activity is not important. What's important is for you to interact with others and get back into society in some capacity. Ok?"

I'm sure my eyes are as big as saucers. Just the thought of a social gathering increases my anxiety but I reluctantly agree. He writes on his notepad, then rips off half a sheet and gives it to me. On it he's written the names of a couple agencies that offer online PTSD coaching. "These two resources have gotten great reviews. If these don't work for you just give me a call and I'll help you find a different agency. How's that sound?"

"That sounds great actually," I smile. The first genuine one to cross my lips in months. I no longer feel like the butt of someone's joke or fodder for gossip. Dr. Washington seems to really care. For the first time since this whole ordeal began, I feel empowered. We schedule an appointment for next week and he walks me back through the maze of offices to the lobby. I'm so happy I could grab him in a bear hug and squeeze him tight. I manage to contain myself though. We shake hands and I am off to face the world again. This time, with a plan.

Chapter 13

I immediately text my family and invite them to go bowling this Saturday at 2PM. Or I guess I don't so much "invite" them as announce:

> "I'll be at Bowl-O-Rama Saturday at 2 if anyone wants to join me. Hope to see y'all."

With that done I head home to rest. Being open and vulnerable is absolutely draining. When I wake up from my nap it's nightfall. I lay out my clothes for work tomorrow, fix dinner, and get back in the bed.

On Saturday, I am over the moon about the get to-gether. It will be nice to spend a day with family just hanging out and starting to put things back in place. I carefully choose an outfit that is casual yet chic. Baby blue skinny jeans with a lightweight, peach colored pullover. I pair it with a gold jewelry set which matches my skin tone. A natural makeup look with bronzer and body glitter gives my skin a sun-kissed glow and I am off to the bowling alley by 1:00PM.

I arrive at 1:30 and reserve the two lanes farthest from the door. That gives us a little bit of privacy and places us close to the concession stand and bar. I'm not sure if alcohol is a good or bad idea, but it's here either way. I grab some munchies and kick my feet up to watch sports clips on the monitors while I wait. Family members start arriving around 2:20. Not too bad, considering we are always late. We all hug and I'm thankful this reception is better than the apprehension or avoidance I've gotten the past couple of months. So far, so good.

Quite a few people show up - my parents, brothers, nieces, several cousins - fourteen of us in total. Casual greetings of 'How have you been?' and 'What have you been up to?' get sprinkled around. After the pleasantries, we split into two groups and everyone dons their shoes and gets their bowling balls ready. We put our information into the scoring consoles and the games begin.

Everything starts off easy. Someone orders pizza and pitchers of beer and soda for the group and the party starts to liven up. Food always makes everything better. Alcohol, not so much. I look around and notice that Mom and Brandon are a bit detached from the festivities. I go over to see how they're doing. "Why are you two huddled over here all by yourselves? What's the matter?"

"Nothing's the matter, Hope." Mom says. She never calls me that so I know right away there's a problem.

"Well, you are unusually quiet. You don't seem to be enjoying yourself. So out with it! What's wrong?" I try again.

"I just don't know why you couldn't let me keep the bedroom set. They came to take the bed while I was still laying in it! And I can't believe you would file a fraud claim against your brother. The credit card companies have been hounding him for months! You have truly disappointed me, Hope. I raised you better than this."

I look at her in disbelief, rapidly blinking and trying to compute what I just heard. "I almost died and you're sitting here talking about the stuff you didn't get to keep when I ended up being inconveniently alive! Are you fucking kidding me!?!"

That gets the attention of the rest of the family who quickly make their way over to our sitting area. "Who are you talking to? I know you're not talking to my aunt like that?" someone screams. That's all it takes for the entire group to erupt into a shouting match. Everybody seems mad at everybody. Screaming, finger pointing, and shoving ensues. I make my way out of the chaos and look back at my family in horror. This family outing definitely didn't go the way I envisioned. With disappointment in my heart, I grab my purse and slip out the front door as the elderly rent-a-cop ambles over to the crowd. *I sure hope he has backup coming. With my family, he's going to need it.*

I spend the rest of the weekend curled in bed feeling sorry for myself. Everything is such a mess. Sunday night, as a rainstorm deluges the city, I get an idea. I'll take a vacation. I need to put some distance between this town and me. I pick up my phone and check Priceline for cheap vacations. Turns out Maui isn't too pricey this time of year. I search for a villa that will allow me to be as secluded as possible and end up booking a flight and hotel package for under $2000. Not bad for last minute. I text my boss letting him know that I'm taking the week off. I grab a couple bags and start throwing in summer dresses, swimsuits, and flip flops. Hair products, sun screen, and toiletries are tossed into my small carry on. Then I download some movies to my iPad for the long travel day tomorrow. I take a hot bath and crawl back in bed, falling asleep to the soothing sounds of Luther.

* * * *

The next morning I take a quick shower, fluff my twist-out, and throw my bags in the trunk. I make a quick last-minute pass through the house and am out the door by 9:00AM. My flight leaves at 12:39PM so there is ample time to have a nice hearty breakfast and get to the airport two hours before departure. Everything goes as planned and by 1:30PM my plane is in the air and a drink is in my hand. I turn on a movie and nod on and off until we are on the final approach into Maui. After getting lei'd I catch a taxi to the property which is even more beautiful than the online advertisements conveyed. The hotel clerk checks me in and I go straight to the villa. I drop my bags by the entrance and nearly skip to the balcony to open the door and let in the fresh air. There's a nice view of the courtyard, pool, and a peek of the ocean. I leave the glass door open and fall out on the sofa where I sleep for hours.

When I wake I feel rested and refreshed, better than I've felt in ages. It's dark outside but the courtyard and pool area are lit up festively. I shower, change, and head out for a walk around the property. Plenty of trails and passages meander throughout the immaculately landscaped grounds. After a long walk I stop at the hotel restaurant for dinner and then lounge in one of the hammocks and listen to the waves crash for hours. Over the next week I enjoy horseback riding, water sports, and beachside massages. In the evenings I take long walks around the property or sit and look out into the ocean. I get a lot of thinking done and by the end of the week, I've made some tough but necessary decisions.

Chapter 14

I get back in town Sunday evening. When I open my door, the still-unpacked boxes greet me. Ignoring them, I throw my luggage in the closet, take a long hot shower and go to bed.

When I go to work the next day I don't go straight to my office as usual. Instead I go to the Human Resources Department and talk to one of the specialists.

"Hi, I'm Hope McKinley." I hand her my badge so she can look up my employee ID.

"Hi Hope! How are you?"

"I've been better."

She bites her lips and averts her eyes. "Yes, I heard you've been having a rough couple of months."

I'm pretty sure that's NOT something she was supposed to tell me but I let it slide. Offices, especially human resources departments, are rumor mills. It would be silly to think that my situation somehow escaped these gossip channels.

"How can I help you? Are you referring someone to our organization?"

"No. The opposite actually. I want to know what my options are if I leave. What am I entitled to? What happens to my retirement? That sort of thing."

"Are you thinking about leaving? We would hate to see you go. You've been such an asset here. I know your readjustment has been difficult. Maybe you just need a vacation —."

"Actually, I just came back from one. I appreciate the kind words but I'm not so sure everyone here shares your sentiment. Please, can you just let me know my options?"

She keys in my employee number to bring up my profile and turns her computer screen so I can see it. "If you were to leave in, let's say two weeks, you still have 32 days of sick leave accrued and 11 days of unused vacation. All of that would be paid in a lump sum. Your pension plan currently has a balance of $246,901. You can leave your pension in the account to be managed by the city until you reach retirement age. Or you can take a lump sum payout, which will be penalized since you haven't reached retirement age. Your life insurance is not portable so the policy terminates once you resign." I chuckle a bit at that last line. This is the same policy that already had a claim filed against it. I fought to get it back. Now I'm losing it again. Thankfully she misses the irony.

She clicks some more keys on her keyboard and a figure pops up. "This is an estimate of what your total payout would be if you terminated employment two weeks from to-day." I'm stunned. Even with all the penalties it's still a really nice figure. I'm still young. I can rebuild my retirement fund. Right now I feel the need to take the money and run, so to speak. "What do I need to do to officially put in my notice?"

She looks genuinely sad but dutifully pulls out a form and hands it to me. "You can either fill out this Resignation Form, or send an email to your supervisor from your employee email account with this information included. Either way, once I receive notice of your official resignation, I can begin to prepare your separation package."

"I'll just fill out the form now since I'm already here." I respond.

"There's no rush. You can take it home and think about it," she says hopefully.

I shake my head. "There's nothing to think about." I finish filling out the form and hand it back to her.

She makes me a copy for my records and sets the original on her desk. "I really do hate to see you go, but I understand. I truly wish you the best." She comes from behind the desk and gives me a big hug. Although I'm sure it's just a combination of sorrow and pity, I appreciate the hug nonetheless. When I pull away she has tears in her eyes. We hardly know each other so I'm baffled by her strong reaction. I thank her for her help and leave the office.

I head up to my department to talk to Scott, my boss. He's been very accommodating throughout this entire ordeal. I don't know how he will take the news of my departure, but he deserves to hear it directly from me, not from the rumor mill. As I walk through the call center I see Scott buzzing around and stop him between the center cubicles. "Hey, can I talk to you for a minute?"

"Sure, I just need to deliver these reports and I'll be right back. Meet in my office in five?"

"Sure, that's perfect," I reply.

My office is just a couple doors down from his. I park myself at my desk and look around. Accolades for accomplishments line the shelves. Charts of our region hang on the walls. A pile of work in progress covers my desk. Over the past four years, hard work and research have reduced emergency call response times from an atrocious 11 minute average down to a very respectable six. We've streamlined the process so that everyone is on the same page as far as how calls are handled. Overall we've saved thousands of lives.

I'm really proud of my work as a city statistician. Even before the incident, though, I yearned for something more. A position with the federal government would be a great leap. A position with the NFL would be a dream come true. Either way, those career shifts aren't likely to happen if I stay behind a desk in Springfield, KS. I've made quite a mark here. Now it's time to pursue larger, more fulfilling opportunities.

A few minutes go by and Scott taps on my door. "You ready?"

"Yeah, I'll be there in a sec." He whizzes off to his office and

I trudge behind him. I shut the door and take a seat on one of the basic, tattered chairs that furnish his office.

"What's up?" He's so upbeat. I hate to burst his bubble but there's no sense in beating around the bush.

"I put in my two weeks notice earlier today," I blurt out.

He nods his head but doesn't necessarily look surprised. "Yeah, I expected you would at some point."

"Really?" I'm shocked.

"Sure. You really haven't adjusted well since ... you came back. And I can't blame you. I know it hasn't been easy for you. A person can only be unhappy for so long."

I quietly nod in agreement. "You're right. I mean, I do love it here. It's just that I want more. I love my career and being close to my family, as dysfunctional as they can be. I just don't want to be stuck in Springfield all my life. Even though this whole ordeal sucked, I think it was just the kick in the pants I needed to stop wasting life and pursue my dreams."

A tear trickles down my face. Scott offers kind words and understanding while I pull myself together. He asks if I'll be using my sick leave and vacation time to cover my last two weeks. "Not all of it. Maybe just next week. I want to organize my projects so my replacement can hit the ground running. I also need to say bye to everyone before I leave. I'll pack next week."

"Ohh, so you're moving immediately?"

"Yes. I decided I need a complete change of scenery. Someplace where no one knows me and I can start fresh."

He nods again. "Yeah, that makes sense. Well, I hope this fresh start brings everything you desire."

"Thank you," I say, tears welling up again. I leave Scott's office before they fall. Back in my office I pull out last month's response time chart and compare data to the same time last year. Consistent improvements. That makes me proud.

The next week flies by in a blur. When I get to work on Friday, balloons decorate the office and everyone is in a festive mood. They scream a lively SURPRISE as I walk in and I burst into tears. I wasn't expecting a going away party. A catered lunch and specialty cake arrive mid-day. Some of my closer colleagues give me presents and gift cards to wish me well.

I am touched by the sweet gesture and planning that went into this. We all enjoy a relaxed day at the office, or as relaxed as things can be in an emergency call center. When the day is done I'm loaded down with things from my office, gifts, cards, and leftover food. I am so grateful for the people who went above and beyond to show they care. A few treasured friends even offer to come by and help me pack up my place. I don't hesitate to take them up on the offer. Although quite a bit of my life is still boxed up from when my family haphazardly returned my belongings, a lot of packing still remains and I could definitely use the help.

Chapter 15

In the midst of packing, I get a call that sends me into a tail-spin. "Hi, this is Stacy from Johnson Family Funeral Homes. I'm just calling to let you know the death certificates for Hope McKinley are here. Do you want to pick them up or do you want us to mail them?"

"Thank you for letting me know. I'll be right over to pick them up."

I go to the funeral home to pick up the copies. The same funeral attendant is there, and she recognizes me immediately. She opens her mouth to speak but I beat her to it. "Hi, Cin. Stacy called a little while ago to let me know my death certificates are ready for pick up." She rocks back on her kitten heels, camel colored this time, and puts her hands on her hips. She turns and yells, "STACY!"

"Yelling across the lobby now. So uncouth." I laugh as she glares in my direction. She can't even fake professionalism at this point. I sense an ass chewing coming Stacy's way.

Mrs. Johnson, the funeral director's wife, hears the yelling and comes bouncing down the staircase. "Cin! What's all that yelling abou—." She sees me and stops mid-sentence. Her bounce quickens to a trot. She reaches the landing and nearly sprints across the lobby to get in my face. "You. Nearly. Killed. My. HUSBAND! I should get a restraining order against you for that stunt you pulled!" she scolds.

I laugh uncontrollably. "YOU should get a restraining order against ME! You tried to bury me alive! If anything it's me that should have a restraining order against YOU! Matter of fact, maybe I should call the health department and have them come and check your so-called corpses. I'd hate for one of your clients to really be alive and not have the good fortune to wake up in time like I did!"

A look of indignation plasters her face. She has the losing hand and she knows it. She turns and storms down the main hallway. She's probably going to cuss somebody out. I giggle to myself.

A short while later a young woman hurries out of the same door Mrs. Johnson entered. She's clutching her coat and purse to her chest as she walks towards me with her head hung low. As she gets closer I can see tears streaming down her face. I'm guessing this is Stacy. Without a word she blows past me and flings open the lobby doors. Less than a minute later I hear tires squeal out of the parking lot. A piece of me feels a little bad for her. This whole mixup wasn't *her* fault. At this point my name should be etched in everyone's brain, and they should know not to call me. Clearly someone didn't train her properly.

It's obvious that my getting assistance is going to take a while so I lounge on one of the round sofas in the lobby. They really are gaudy looking things. Big, round, rose gold couches trimmed in gold. I roll my eyes at the situation and the decor. Cin eventually comes huffing down the lengthy hallway. Again, there's no professionalism wasted on me. When she reaches me she shoves an envelope in my hand. "These are the death certificates. I believe our business is done."

"That's it?" I scoff. "No apologies? No nothing? You act like all of this is MY fault." She resumes her glare but doesn't say anything further. I stand to leave. "You just handed me my own death certificate. Our business is far from done." I turn to exit. Clearly I'm not getting anything more from this bunch. I leave the funeral home surprisingly much calmer than I did the last time and head home.

* * * *

I pick up my mail on the way to my apartment. Once inside I throw my keys, mail, and the envelope from the funeral home on the coffee table. I drag myself into the kitchen and pour a glass of wine, then turn on the tv and plop on the couch. Channel surfing is fruitless. Even after all this time nothing holds my attention. HGTV is as good a channel as any for background noise. My eyes are on the tv, but that envelope is in my peripheral view and it's calling to me. I grab it and rip it open. My heart sinks. Looking at this document finally makes my entire ordeal real. *I was declared dead. I was almost buried alive. What if ...?* I shake my head and push those thoughts away. It's pointless to wonder what ifs. The fact is, I did wake up in time! I have to stay focused on that and be grateful.

I browse through the rest of the mail with disinterest. Nothing but the usual - cable bill, electric bill, student loan bill, phone bill. I start to put the mail down and jolt to attention. I look at the student loan bill and the death certificate. Suddenly another thought comes to me. What does it take to get student loans discharged? Maybe the only thing they need is ... a death certificate. I look down at the document again, this time not with horror but intrigue. *Could that work? I mean, after the loans are discharged, would they really follow up to see if I was actually alive? Hmm.* My mind spins at the possibility. I travel through this fantasy world for a moment, then integrity and honesty snap me back to reality. I don't want to go from casket to C-Block. That may make for a great storyline in a movie, but would certainly be a bad life choice. I better not risk it.

I fold the certificates and put them back in the envelope. I throw everything back on the coffee table and pick up my wine and the remote. In an instant, Netflix is cued up. Time to settle in for another sleepless night. Tomorrow I must remember to send a copy of the death certificate to the law office so they can work on getting it invalidated.

Chapter 16

My last week in town goes by in a flash. There's barely enough time to get everything accomplished. Thankfully my packing help did come through. The apartment is completely boxed up. However, I still need to turn off the utilities, return cable & modem equipment, and a million other last minute things that come with uprooting your life.

On Tuesday afternoon one of the associate attorneys from Walsh & Edelman calls with an update on the case. A formal claim was filed with the city which was swiftly denied. Walsh & Edelman then filed a lawsuit on my behalf against the city and the funeral home. Although the city has yet to respond, Johnson Family Funeral Homes promptly filed a countersuit. Not only are they <u>not</u> willing to accept responsibility for their incompetence, they are doubling down on their insistence that I pay for the unnecessary services rendered. I bite my tongue as he reads me the laundry list of damages the funeral home claims they suffered. Funeral costs including the full cost of the casket, flowers, and limos, damage to the chapel as people fled in a panic, and medical bills stemming from Mr. Johnson's heart attack. Currently, the damages total two million dollars. The attorney informs me that this total may increase later to reflect additional repairs, doctor visits, and rehab bills. The funeral home also has not listed the estimation for Mr. Johnson's loss of earnings damages.

If this is the route they want to take, fine. I'm ready for war.

I thank the attorney and make sure the office has my new address, a UPS Mailbox that offers forwarding services so I don't have to miss anything important. He confirms my contact information and wishes me a safe journey. I'm disappointed the situation has gotten this far but am resolute in my decision to see my case through to the end.

The movers come on Thursday to pack my items in containers and transport them to a storage facility in DC. I plan to spend some time driving through the midwest and parts of Canada before heading down to our nation's capital. Despite the hectic nature of these past two weeks I did manage to apply for several jobs with various government agencies. I don't expect them to move fast on processing the applications. Many listings have close dates up to three months from now. Thankfully, with my payout I have enough funds to last me several years if need be.

When the last of my boxes are on the moving truck I throw my luggage in the car. I watch the moving truck pull off with pretty much my entire life inside. I follow behind, making a brief stop at the leasing office. When I enter I see the leasing staff laughing amongst themselves. I approach Stephanie, the assistant manager.

"I'm moving out. For real this time." I laugh and they chuckle right along with me. I hand over the keys and my form with the forwarding address. They too wish me well and we exchange hugs as I depart.

Once back in my car I pull up my music app, shuffle my catalog, and settle in for a leisurely months-long road trip. Ultimately, I want a fresh start where people don't know me or my story. That will come in time. For now I will hit the open road, get lost in my thoughts, and decompress from this sordid ordeal. I turn out of the apartment complex and hit the highway. I put my old life in the rearview mirror and head due north, on the road to healing.

Sowing the seeds of love and hope
Love and hope
We don't have to stay
Stuck in the way

Have I the courage to change today

Artist: P!nk
Album: Hurts 2B Human
Track 8: Courage
Composers: Alecia Moore,
Sia Furler,
Greg Kurstin
2019

Afterward

There are so many necessary conversations that never get discussed, especially in the Black community, either out of fear or taboo. Through Hope's story I aimed to gently touch on several points.

First, everyone should give some consideration to what will happen when you pass away. Everybody should have some type of estate plan - at the very least, a well crafted will to let your loved ones know who will inherit your possessions. For those who have a specific vision for your funeral, or if you prefer cremation, you should have your funeral plan in writing so it is clear and indisputable.

Second, there can be great value in therapy. In fact, I think most people can benefit from some form of therapy. Life can be grueling. It can help to have an objective professional guide you through tough moments so that you can heal and thrive.

Last, if you don't like some aspect of your life, change it.

To truly be happy you have to design and follow your own path. If there is a desire tugging at your heart that won't let you go, that is probably the direction you are supposed to go in. It's ok to move, change careers, or follow that dream you hold dear - even when everyone else tells you you're crazy. Well, I mean - if you have children you should feed them, LOL. But once you and your family's immediate needs (food, clothing, safety, shelter) are taken care of, work on nurturing yourself. Life is too short to put yourself aside. Chase your dreams. Get to happy as soon as you can and never let go of it.

Acknowledgements

To my mom: I wish you were here to share in this moment. Thank you for your gentle love and motherly sacrifices. I never envisioned a time when you wouldn't be here. I miss you every day.

To my dad: Thank you for being a provider and demonstrating a strong work ethic. I'm sure a great deal of my tenacity stems from the example you set.

To DJ, Floyd, Kenny, and Gordon - my much older brothers who are so so much older than I am {giggles}: Each of you hold a special place in my heart, individually and collectively. You are my first friends, protectors, confidantes. Thank you for loving me and always cheering my dreams. I love you all endlessly.

To Winnie, Cynthia, Pam, and Ayeasha: I've always wanted a sister. Mom said I was lucky to be here and a sister wasn't happening. Thankfully you all came along and filled that role. Thank you for the love and support throughout the years. Terry, you've been a delightful addition to the family. Thank you for being a cheerleader.

To my day ones: Jarvis "76 Keys" Smith and Brandon Thornton (and no, Brandon, the character in the book is not named after you - haha). Even though we don't talk much, you are always there when I need you and you are both so very much appreciated.

To my Nieces/Nephews/Great-Nieces/Great-Nephews & my beautiful Goddaughter Dasia: I can be so disconnected and I know it. You may not see me very much but I think of you often and love you all immensely.

To my Godmother Bonnie Flagg: Some family is chosen. I'm so glad we met and chose each other. You are one of the brightest lights in my life. I love you more than mere words can convey.

To my extended Gilkes, Wheeler, and Leslie families: Thank you all for the love. I treasure every moment I spend with you in the US, Toronto, Barbados, and beyond.

To Andi Scully and Macario James: Thank you both for introducing me to the wonderful concept that is NaNoWriMo. Without that platform this novella may have taken even longer to become a reality. W.T. Council, thank you for reading the first draft. Your notes helped this story take form.

To Dianne Hunter: You are amazing! Thank you for serving as my editor. I appreciate all the hard work you put into polishing this manuscript. You brought so much value to this project and I sincerely appreciate you.

To Anthony Robinson: Thank you for paving the way and offering guidance throughout every step of my journey. You are a gem.

To Malik M.L. Williams: Your friendship is a gift that I cherish dearly. Thank you for being my sounding board and shoulder to lean on.

To Camille Corbin: The best concert buddy on the planet. Thank you for the love, support, and advice. And, for being my concert sidekick. You are so appreciated.

To my Friends: Your never-ending support is my lifeline. Your excitement and encouragement of my various projects has carried me through many rough and uncertain moments.

To my Facebook Family: I am unapologetically addicted to Facebook. To those in my circle, thank you for the laughs, tears, advice, and thought-provoking dilemmas. Your posts entertain, inspire, make me angry, make me think. Facebook is truly an introvert's dream. Thank you for sharing your life on such a public forum. I enjoy watching you all ... from afar. LOL

To my Toastmasters® Family: Special thanks to Greg Pick, First Rate Toastmasters, and District 25; Nubian Voices Toastmasters, Jackpot Speakers, and all those who have supported me from Central California & Southern Nevada Districts 33 and 115; Witty Storytellers and my online Toastmasters community. Thank you Sherrie Parker for serving as my mentor and offering guidance and friendship. Thank you Marie O'Connor for the gentle kick in the @ss.

To Michelle Words: Thank you for your friendship and

for amping up my travel experiences by introducing me to
Nomadness Travel Tribe. Through tribe I've met two amazing souls - Kenna Williams, not only have you made me a
believer in group travel, you've helped to restore my faith in
humanity. The amount of compassion you possess is mind
blowing. So many people's lives are better simply because
they were fortunate enough to cross your path. Thank you
for being a light in so much darkness. Sylvia Roldán, my
tribe sister turned Toastmasters sister! You are such a joy to
be around. Thank you for sharing in my love of life, travel,
and Toastmasters journeys.

To my Texas Wesleyan University School of Law family:
Law school is the most grueling yet rewarding hazing experience ever. I cherish the judges, professors, and classmates
who became friends along the way. I couldn't have been
bonded with a better group of people. The Tarrant County
legal community is so nurturing. I am blessed to have my
legal roots planted there.

To Aerica Raven Van Dorn: The journey to this book
cover was a seven month ordeal. Thank you for being the light
at the end of the tunnel. Your concept and design are a perfect
showcasing for my story. To Darlene of Van-Garde Imagery,
Inc., thank you for helping to put the final pieces of the puz-
zle in place. The interior design is lovely and if it weren't for
you I would still be watching YouTube videos trying to figure
out how to upload my book and get it to the masses.

To those who have helped behind the scenes with branding/imaging: the ones that handle the left side of my head - Kiki Hair Braiding, the one that handles the right side of my head - Leo my barber, webmaster Megan Tegtmeyer, photographer Robert Somadhi, and marketing/promotion assistants. In your own way all of you have helped to make this project a success and I thank you.

Last but certainly not least, thank you, Dear Reader. Your support is so very treasured. I hope this book inspired you to heal any lingering wounds from your past, cherish every day, and go in the direction of your own dreams.

If there is anyone I missed ... "Love Me Anyway."

Nadia Gilkes is a proud graduate of Texas Wesleyan University School of Law. She is licensed to practice in Texas where she primarily focuses on family law and estate planning. She spends her time between the DFW Metroplex and Las Vegas, NV. In her spare time she enjoys quilting, arts & crafts festivals, and following P!nk around the country.

Made in United States
Orlando, FL
08 December 2023